— INTERACTIONS —

Minds·On PHYSICS

Activities & Reader

— INTERACTIONS —

Minds·On
PHYSICS

Activities & Reader

William J. Leonard
Robert J. Dufresne
William J. Gerace
Jose P. Mestre

The University of Massachusetts
Physics Education Research Group

 KENDALL/HUNT PUBLISHING COMPANY
4050 Westmark Drive   Dubuque, Iowa 52002

Also available in the Minds•On Physics Series

Minds•On Physics: Motion / Activities & Reader

Teacher's Guide to accompany Minds•On Physics: Motion

Minds•On Physics: Interactions / Activities & Reader

Teacher's Guide to accompany Minds•On Physics: Interactions

*Minds•On Physics: Conservation Laws & Concept-Based Problem Solving /
Activities & Reader*

*Teacher's Guide to accompany Minds•On Physics: Conservation Laws &
Concept-Based Problem Solving*

Teacher's Guide to accompany Minds•On Physics: Fundamental Forces & Fields

Minds•On Physics: Complex Systems / Activities & Reader

Teacher's Guide to accompany Minds•On Physics: Complex Systems

Minds•On Physics: Advanced Topics in Mechanics / Activities & Reader

Teacher's Guide to accompany Minds•On Physics: Advanced Topics in Mechanics

Author Address for Correspondence

William J. Leonard
Department of Physics & Astronomy
Box 34525
University of Massachusetts
Amherst, MA 01003–4525 USA

e-mail: WJLEONARD@phast.umass.edu

Cover Photos: Image of roller coaster "The Dragon"
courtesy of Adventureland Park, Des Moines, Iowa.
Tennis player image © 1997 PhotoDisc.
All other images courtesy of Corel.

ISBN 0-7872-3929-1

This book was prepared with the support of NSF Grant: ESI 9255713.
However, any opinions, findings, conclusions and or recommendations herein
are those of the authors and do not necessarily reflect the views of NSF.

Printed in the United States of America
10 9 8 7 6 5 4 3 2

Contents

continued

Activities (continued)

Reader
Chapter 2: Describing Interactions

Reader (continued)

continued

Reader (continued)

Reader (continued)

continued

Reader (continued)

Appendix: Table of Common Forces

How to Use this Book

The activities in this book are designed to get you *thinking about* and *doing* physics — in a way that is a lot closer to the way professional scientists think about and do science. You will learn by communicating your ideas with your teacher and with other students, and by trying to make sense of the ideas presented in the book.

During the school year, you may be required to memorize some definitions, vocabulary, and other basic information, but you should <u>not</u> try to memorize the answers to specific questions and problems. Answers should *make sense to you.* If they do not make sense to you, then you probably should go back and change how you think about the problem or situation. Even if everyone else seems to understand something, please do not give up! Keep trying until it makes sense to you.

We want *everyone* in the class to understand physics, and we sincerely believe that everyone *can* learn to understand physics. The activities in this book are designed to help you *start* developing the skills needed to learn physics. *You* must do the rest. If necessary, your teacher and your classmates should be able to help you. Find out how they think about a problem or situation, and adapt their ideas to your own way of thinking. And if you are helping someone else, remember that everyone learns at a different rate, so please be patient.

This style of learning requires a lot of dedication and work, especially if you are not familiar with the style. In the short run, this style might seem impossible and not worth the extra effort. But in the long run, it is definitely worth it. We really, really want you to memorize *as little as possible.* Focus on the ideas that are most widely useful, and learn how to use these to derive the relationships you might need to answer a question or solve a problem. You will be able to solve lots of problems using this approach, and you will develop skills that will be useful in any field you might choose to enter. Remember that physics is one way — among many — of looking at the natural world. It's a way of analyzing, evaluating, describing, explaining and predicting the behavior of objects and collections of objects.

Acknowledgments

The *concept-based problem-solving* approach to learning is the way Bill Gerace has taught hundreds of graduate and undergraduate students at the University of Massachusetts. It is his approach that has been refined, modified, and adapted to create the activities in this book.

We are deeply grateful to the National Science Foundation for funding the pilot project, *Materials for Developing Concept-Based Problem-Solving Skills in Physics*, under grant MDR–9050213. Although we had no prior experience writing materials for high-school physics, the Foundation reasoned that as experts in both physics and cognitive research, we were uniquely qualified to bring a fresh outlook to the task. We thank NSF also for funding the renewal, *Minds-On Physics: An Integrated Curriculum for Developing Concept-Based Problem Solving in Physics*, under grant ESI–9255713. The materials in this book are a direct result of this funding and are also evidence of how federal support can impact education and stimulate reform. We thank Gerhard Salinger, our project director at NSF, for his unwavering support of our approach and his many suggestions.

We are very fortunate to have found four wonderful teachers who were willing to try a different approach to teaching physics by field-testing those first 24 "modules" of the pilot project: Charlie Camp (Amherst Regional HS, Amherst, MA), Mike Cunha (Weaver HS, Hartford, CT), Steve Degon (Central HS, Springfield, MA) and Hughes Pack (Northfield–Mount Hermon School, Northfield, MA). They let us into their classrooms and let us see first-hand how their students dealt with the approach. Their numerous suggestions have improved the materials and the approach greatly.

We also thank all the teachers who have field-tested the Minds•On Physics activities: Jane Barrett (Howard School of Academics & Technology, Chattanooga, TN), Larry Blanchard (Warren Easton HS, New Orleans, LA), Roger Blough (Tyner HS, Chattanooga, TN), Gaby Blum (Monument Mountain Regional HS, Great Barrington, MA), Charlie Camp (ARHS), Jim Carter (Saugus HS, Saugus, MA), Jack Czajkowski (Pioneer Valley Regional School District, MA), John Dark (Brainerd HS, Chattanooga, TN), Steve Degon (Central HS), Ed Eckel (NMH), Jen DuBois (NMH), Jake Foster (Hixson HS, Hixson, TN), Bill Fraser (Chattanooga Phoenix School 3, Chattanooga, TN), Ken Gano (Hixson HS), Dennis Gilbert (Taconic HS, Pittsfield, MA), Craig Hefner (NMH), Ray Janke (Chicopee HS, Chicopee, MA), Aaron Kropf (ARHS), Bernie Lally (Chicopee HS), Michael Oliphant (Millis HS, Millis, MA), Hughes Pack (NMH), Jerry

Pate (Chattanooga School for Arts and Sciences, Chattanooga, TN), Kirk Rau (Tyner HS), Jessie Royal (Dade County HS, Trenton, GA), Cheryl Ryan (Hoosac Valley Regional HS, Adams, MA), John Safko (The University of South Carolina), Glenda Schmidt (Slidell HS, Slidell, LA), Lisa Schmitt (NMH), Steve Schultheis (Saugus HS), Lance Simpson (NMH), Mark Walcroft (Taconic HS), Mark Wenig (CSAS), Maxine Willis (Gettysburg HS, Gettysburg, PA), Melany O'Connor (NMH), and Tom Winn (McMain HS, New Orleans, LA). They often had little warning about what and when materials would arrive, and usually had just a few days to prepare themselves to do the activities in class. We appreciate their patience and understanding. We also thank them for recommending that we create extensive teacher support materials. Although this addition has nearly doubled the scope of the project, it is a welcome change, and every teacher who uses the Minds•On Physics materials is indebted to them.

We thank Kris Chapman and Maggie Coffin for many of the drawings used in the activities. They brought a style and grace to the figures that none of us could ever match. We thank Ian Beatty for creating the Town of King's Court. We also thank Gary Bradway (Berkshire Community College, Pittsfield, MA), for his frequent help with conceptualizing and revising the early activities; Jerry Touger (Curry College, Milton, MA), for his help writing the Reader; and George Collison (The Concord Consortium, Concord, MA), for showing us how hands-on activities may be combined with minds-on activities.

Thanks to Allan Feldman (University of Massachusetts, Amherst, MA) and the rest of his evaluation team (Karla, Jim, Ed, Sonal, and Aaron) for evaluating the materials and its implementation.

We are thankful to Kendall/Hunt for publishing these materials. We are particularly thankful to the people at K/H for their many ideas and suggestions, especially regarding the format and style of these materials.

Special thanks also to all our friends and relatives.

Bill Leonard
Bob Dufresne
Bill Gerace
Jose Mestre

The UMass Physics Education Research Group
Department of Physics & Astronomy
Box 34525
University of Massachusetts
Amherst, MA 01003–4525 USA

Visit us on the Web at http://www-perg.phast.umass.edu/

Activities

36–40:
VECTORS

— & —

41–70:
INTERACTIONS

Introducing Vectors

Purpose and Expected Outcome

You have studied several quantities that have both magnitude and direction. Some of these quantities are used to describe motion, such as position, velocity and acceleration. Others, such as force, are used to describe interactions. Quantities that have both magnitude and direction are called *vectors*. All vector quantities can be described (or represented) in similar ways. The purpose of this activity is to explore some of these similarities. After completing this activity you will be able to:

(a) recognize a vector quantity;

(b) use vectors to describe physical quantities such as position, velocity, and acceleration; and

(c) represent a vector as a magnitude & direction and as a directed line segment.

Prior Experience / Knowledge Needed

A vector is a quantity having both a *magnitude* (size, number, amount) and *direction* (up, down, right, North, Southeast, toward the nearest pizza place). On the other hand, a *scalar* (such as temperature and age) has only magnitude. Any quantity that has both a magnitude and a direction can be considered a vector. Physics uses many different vector quantities. In addition to the vector quantities you already know about, you will learn about several more vector quantities, such as momentum, angular momentum and electric field. One could define any number of vector quantities, but physics is only concerned with vectors that are *useful*—useful for describing <u>how</u> objects behave, useful for understanding <u>why</u> they behave that way, and thus useful for <u>solving problems</u>.

MINI-ACTIVITY: Recognizing Vector Quantities

Before we investigate how to represent vectors, let's make sure we understand the difference between vectors and scalars. For each of the quantities listed below, indicate whether it is a vector or a scalar (or neither). Be prepared to explain your choice.

M1. time

M2. distance

M3. displacement

M4. speed

M5. acceleration

M6. mass

M7. volume

M8. density

M9. weight

M10. height

M11. temperature

M12. shape

M13. velocity

M14. position

M15. magnitude of the acceleration

M16. color

M17. length

M18. width

M19. texture

M20. brightness

Background

There are three common ways to represent vectors:

    (1) as a magnitude & direction (the *polar* representation);

    (2) as a directed line segment (the *graphical* representation); and

    (3) as a set of components (the *component* representation).

You already have some experience with each of these representations. In this activity we will focus on representing vectors as a magnitude & direction, and as a directed line segment. We will come back to components in the next activity.

THE POLAR REPRESENTATION (MAGNITUDE & DIRECTION)

In the polar representation, we describe a vector by explicitly stating its magnitude and direction. We provide an example for displacement. Consider a box that is moved from point *A* to point *B* along the path shown:

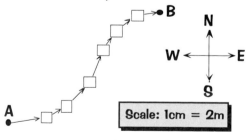

The *magnitude* of the displacement vector is defined to be the shortest distance between points A and B. Using a scale of 1cm = 2m, the magnitude is 10m, as shown at the right. Note that the magnitude does not depend on the orientation of the line connecting A and B.

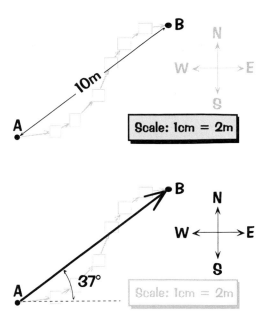

The *direction* of the displacement vector is defined to be the direction of the ray that starts at point A and passes through point B. In this case, the direction is 37° North of East. Note here that the direction does not depend on the scale.

A convenient way to present this information is as follows: (10m, 37°). Written this way the angle is assumed to be measured counterclockwise from the East- (or x-) axis.

THE GRAPHICAL REPRESENTATION (DIRECTED LINE SEGMENT)

In general, a directed line segment is a line segment with an arrowhead at one end. The length of the line segment indicates the <u>magnitude</u> of the vector, and we orient the line segment so that the arrowhead points in the <u>direction</u> of the vector.

Remember two key points about representing vectors with directed line segments. First, you need a *scale* which tells you how the length of the line segment relates to the magnitude of the vector. For example, here are two directed line segments:

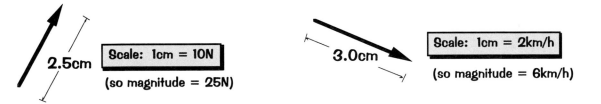

Second, you <u>do not</u> have to be concerned with <u>where</u> a directed line segment is placed; as long as the length and orientation are correct, the magnitude and direction of the vector are completely specified. Any of the directed line segments at the right could be used to represent a force of 26N in the Northeast direction, since they all have the same length (magnitude) and orientation (direction).

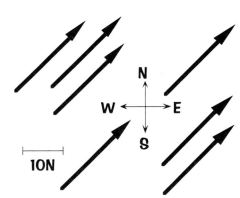

Note that in the polar representation, this vector is written (26N, 45°).

Explanation of Activity and Example

In this activity, we give you descriptions of various people's movements through the imaginary town of King's Court. A map of King's Court is given at the end of this activity (page 143). Use a ruler to determine the lengths of all relevant distances. (Be sure to use the scale shown on the map!) On a copy of the map, draw a directed line segment and use a protractor to determine each vector's direction. Specify the direction as the number of degrees counterclockwise from East. For example, a vector pointing East has a direction of 0°; North is 90°; West is 180°; and South is 270°.

PART A: Determining the Directions of Vector Quantities

For each situation described below, specify the direction of the vector indicated.

A1. The position of the Fire Station, relative to the lower, left corner of the map.

A2. The position of the Snack Shack, relative to the lower, right corner of the map.

A3. The position of the Fire Station, relative to Town Hall.

A4. The displacement of someone traveling from the Grocery Store to the Post Office via Town Hall.

A5. The displacement of someone going from the Fire Station to the Public Beach.

A6. The velocity of someone traveling along Sixth Avenue.

A7. The velocity of someone traveling from Town Hall to the Key Store.

A8. The average velocity of someone traveling from Jam 'n' Jellies to the Grocery Store without traveling along Jordan Heights.

A9. The acceleration of someone slowing down on Jordan Heights as they approach Town Hall.

PART B: Determining Both the Magnitude and Direction of a Vector Quantity

For each of the situations presented below, find the magnitude and the direction of the vector quantity indicated.

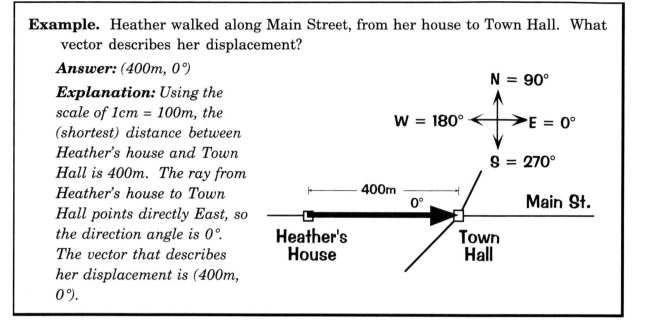

Example. Heather walked along Main Street, from her house to Town Hall. What vector describes her displacement?

Answer: (400m, 0°)

Explanation: Using the scale of 1cm = 100m, the (shortest) distance between Heather's house and Town Hall is 400m. The ray from Heather's house to Town Hall points directly East, so the direction angle is 0°. The vector that describes her displacement is (400m, 0°).

B1. What is the position of the Grocery Store relative to the lower, left corner of the map?

B2. What is the position of the Sporting Goods Store relative to Town Hall?

B3. The Mayor rides a bus from the Fire Station to the Grocery Store by way of Town Hall. What is her displacement?

B4. Deb rides her motorcycle at a constant speed of 30km/h from Town Hall to the Magic Shop going past Heather's house along the way. What is her velocity as she passes Heather's house?

B5. Jerome rides his bike from the Public Beach to the Grocery Store in 6 minutes.
(a) What is his displacement for this trip?
(b) What is his average velocity for this trip?
(c) If Jerome rides at a constant speed during the whole trip, what is his velocity while on Sixth Avenue? Explain.

continued

B6. Heather walks from her home to Town Hall, and later returns home.

   (a) What is her overall displacement?

   (b) What is her average velocity for the trip?

B7. Pierre is driving down Chicago Boulevard at 36km/h (10m/s) when the traffic light at Jump Street turns red. If it takes him 4 seconds to come to a complete stop, what is his average acceleration during this time interval?

Reflection

R1. Under what conditions is the average velocity for a trip equal to zero?

R2. Under what conditions (if any) is the direction of the displacement vector for a particular process <u>different</u> from the direction of the average velocity vector for the same process?

R3. Does the average velocity depend upon the path followed? Explain.

R4. In what ways does the direction of a vector depend upon the choice of origin?

R5. Imagine the following scenario: Yesterday, you traveled from Jam 'n' Jellies to Town Hall via Heather's House with an average velocity of (7m/s, 34°). Could you now travel along Jordan Heights and have the <u>same</u> average velocity for the same trip? How? Would you travel faster, slower or have the same speed during the trip as before? Explain.

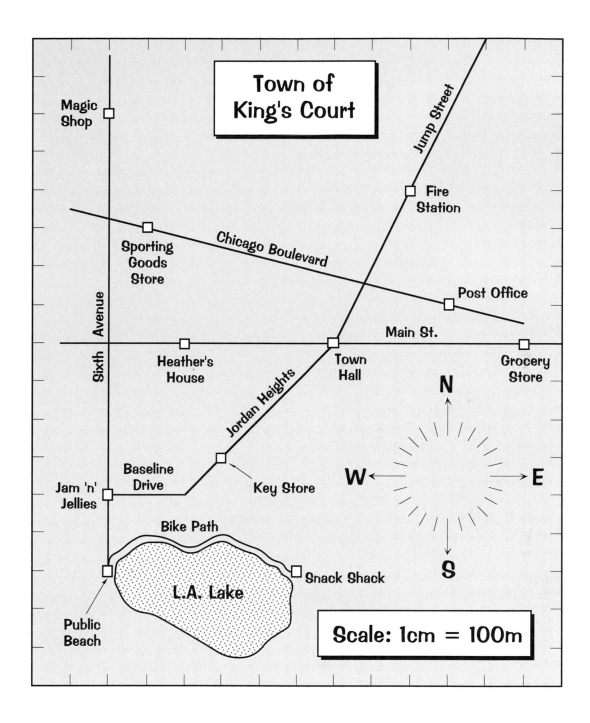

Town of
King's Court

Magic Shop

Jump Street

Fire Station

Chicago Boulevard

Sporting Goods Store

Sixth Avenue

Post Office

Main St.

Heather's House

Town Hall

Grocery Store

N

Jordan Heights

W — E

Baseline Drive

Key Store

Jam 'n' Jellies

S

Bike Path

Snack Shack

L.A. Lake

Public Beach

Scale: 1cm = 100m

Representing Vectors Using Components

Purpose and Expected Outcome

Upon completing this activity, you should be able to represent a vector as a set of components. You should also be able to relate the component representation to other vector representations such as the polar and the graphical representations.

Prior Experience / Knowledge Needed

You will need a protractor and a ruler (marked off in centimeters) to do this activity.

REPRESENTING A VECTOR AS A SET OF COMPONENTS

So far, we have represented a vector as a magnitude and a direction, and as a directed line segment. There are other ways to represent a vector; the only condition on a representation is that it must give you enough information to determine the vector's magnitude and direction.

The three <u>main</u> representations for vectors are:

      (a) as a magnitude and a direction (the polar representation);

      (b) as a directed line segment (the graphical representation); and

      (c) as a set of components (the component representation).

The first two should already be familiar to you. In the component representation, one specifies a vector by stating the "amount" of the vector in each of two different directions. By convention, these two different directions are perpendicular to each other. We will use East and North (or x and y) as the two directions. Formally, the component of a vector along a particular direction is found from the *projection* of the vector onto a line in that direction.

What do we mean by "projecting" a vector along a particular direction?

Consider the following example for a displacement vector of magnitude 2.2cm and direction 27° South of East, as shown to the right.

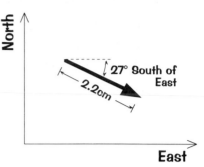

To find the component of the vector along an easterly direction, imagine shining a flashlight on the vector. The flashlight is pointed either North or South so that the vector casts a shadow on the West/East line. The magnitude of the projection onto the West/East line is the length of the vector's shadow. In our example, this length is 2cm, as shown below.

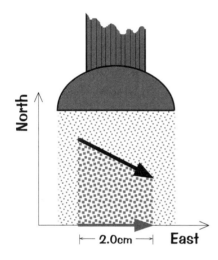

We also need to know whether the projection points in the easterly or westerly direction. By convention, we say that the East component is positive if the projection points to the East, and the East component is negative if the projection points to the West. (Think of *negative* as *the opposite of*; therefore a negative East component refers to a projection that points the opposite to East, which is West.) Thus, in our example, the East component of the vector is +2cm.

Using a similar approach, we find the component of the vector in the northerly direction. The vector's projection on a South/North line is 1cm toward the South. By convention, we say that North is positive and South is negative. Thus, the North component of our example vector is –1cm. (That is, –1cm North is the same as 1cm South.) The component representation of our vector, then, is specified by the East and North components: (2cm East, –1cm North), or simply (2cm E, –1cm N), or even (2cm, –1cm).

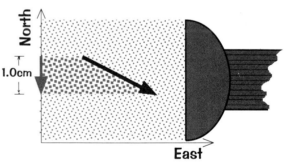

Explanation of Activity and Examples

Each problem in this activity gives you a description of some person's motion through the town of King's Court (see included map on the page 134 of the previous activity). The problem then asks you for a particular position vector, displacement vector, velocity vector, or acceleration vector. You should specify the vector in the component representation.

For displacement vectors, all measurements should be done on the map of King's Court. For velocity and acceleration vectors, enough information is given in each problem to find its components.

Example. Jerome runs along Jump Street from Town Hall to the Fire Station.

(a) Describe his displacement vector.

Answer: $\Delta\mathbf{x} = $ *(200m E, 400m N)*

(b) If it takes Jerome 2 minutes to reach the Fire Station, what is his average velocity for the trip?

Answer: $\mathbf{v}_{\text{ave}} = $ *(1²/₃ m/s E, 3¹/₃ m/s N) — or — (6km/h E, 12km/h N)*

Explanation: The Fire Station is located 200m to the East and 400m to the North of Town Hall. Therefore, the displacement from Town Hall to the Fire Station is (200m E, 400m N).

The average velocity vector is found by dividing the displacement vector by the time elapsed. Therefore, the East component is 200m/2min = 200m/120s = 1²/₃ m/s, or 0.2km/¹/₃₀h = 6km/h. The North component is 400m/2min = 400m/120s = 3¹/₃ m/s, or 0.4km/¹/₃₀h = 12km/h.

A1. Heather rides a bus from the Public Beach to her home.

(a) What is her displacement?

(b) Along Sixth Avenue the bus travels at 20km/h. What is Heather's velocity during this time?

A2. A fire truck leaves the Fire Station and drives to the corner of Main Street and Sixth Avenue by the most direct route.

(a) What is the truck's displacement between the Fire Station and Town Hall?

(b) What is the truck's displacement for the entire trip?

(c) It takes the fire truck 6s to stop at Sixth Avenue starting at 27km/h ($7^{1}/_{2}$m/s). What is the truck's average acceleration during this time interval?

continued

A3. Gary rides his mountain bike from the Grocery Store to the Snack Shack in 1 minute 20 seconds.

(a) What is his average velocity for the trip?

(b) After buying some groceries, Gary now proceeds home such that his average velocity for the entire trip (starting at the Snack Shack) is equal to (0.8km/h E, 2.4km/h N). Assuming that Gary lives 500m (as the crow flies) from the Post Office, what are the possible locations of his home?

Reflection

R1. (a) How many components are needed to fully specify the position of an object? (Keep in mind that the problems in this activity involve objects located on a flat area.)

(b) Can you determine the exact location of an object given <u>only</u> the components of its position? Explain why or why not. If not, what additional information needs to be specified?

R2. How many components are needed to fully specify the velocity of an object? What information (other than its components) is needed? Do you need to know the location of the origin? Explain.

R3. (a) You are told that the East component of a particular vector is negative. What can you say about its direction?

(b) You are then told that the North component of the same vector is positive. What must be true about its direction?

(c) Finally, you are told that the magnitude of its North component is larger than the magnitude of its East component. Now, what must be true about its direction?

Changing Vector Representations

Purpose and Expected Outcome

When solving problems with vectors it is often the case that you know how to describe the vector in one representation, but need a description of the vector in a different representation. For example, you may know a force vector's magnitude and direction, but need to know its components. After completing this activity you will be able to relate each of the three main representations of vectors.

Prior Experience / Knowledge Needed

You should be familiar with the three major representations of vectors.

BASIC MATHEMATICAL RELATIONSHIPS FOR VECTORS

The basic quantities associated with a vector are its *magnitude*, its *direction*, and its *components*. You have used all of these so far, by measuring them for a variety of displacement and velocity vectors. Instead of going through the bother and inaccuracy of drawing and measuring, you can relate these concepts to each other through several simple mathematical relationships. Let's introduce those relationships.

First, some notation: A vector is indicated by a bold-faced symbol, such as **r** for position, **v** for velocity, **a** for acceleration, and **F** for force. The magnitude of a vector is indicated by an italicized symbol, such as r, v, a, and F. Angles are indicated by certain greek symbols, such as θ and ϕ, and components are indicated using certain subscripts, such as x for horizontal components, and y for vertical components. So, for example, the x-component of velocity is v_x, and the y-component of acceleration is a_y. The greek symbol Δ ("delta") is used to indicate the "change in" something. So, $\Delta \mathbf{r}$ is the change in position (i.e., the displacement), and $\Delta \mathbf{v}$ is the change in velocity.

Consider the following situation: A box is pushed to the left using a force **F** directed at an angle ϕ below the horizontal as shown.

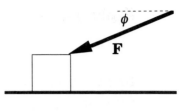

To find the components of the force **F**, we place the directed line segment in an *xy*-coordinate system as shown below.

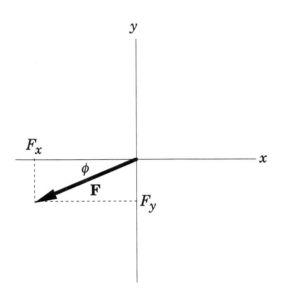

The components of the vector **F** are F_x and F_y. In this case, both are negative. To find relationships between the components and the magnitude and direction, we imagine a right triangle having hypotenuse F and angle ϕ, as shown below.

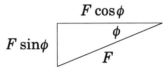

Using trigonometry, we know that the length of the side opposite the angle ϕ is equal to $F \sin\phi$, and the length of the side adjacent to the angle ϕ is equal to $F \cos\phi$. But these lengths are both positive, so we must use common sense to convert the lengths into components, as shown below:

$$F_x = - F \cos\phi$$

$$F_y = - F \sin\phi$$

Although these expressions are <u>not</u> generally applicable to all situations, the technique may be used to find the components of any vector.

When we know the components, we use the pythagorean theorem to find the magnitude:

$$F = \sqrt{(F_x)^2 + (F_y)^2},$$

and trigonometry to find the angle:

$$\tan\phi = \frac{|F_y|}{|F_x|}$$

— or —

$$\phi = \tan^{-1}\frac{|F_y|}{|F_x|}$$

where $|F_y|$ is the absolute value of the *y*-component of **F**, and $|F_x|$ is the absolute value of the *x*-component of **F**.

Explanation of Activity

PART A: Relating Components to Magnitude and Direction

Below are four vectors represented as directed line segments. For each vector (a) determine <u>by measurement</u> its magnitude, direction, x-component, and y-component, then (b) use the measured components to <u>calculate</u> its magnitude and direction. Some values have been provided. **Note:** Direction angles are measured counter-clockwise from the positive x-axis.

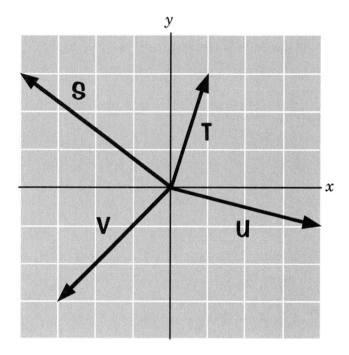

		(a) <u>Measure</u> these quantities from the diagram above.				(b) <u>Calculate</u> these.	
vector		x-comp.	y-comp.	magnitude	direction	magnitude	direction
A1.	S			5cm			
A2.	T		3cm				71.6°
A3.	U	4cm				4.12cm	
A4.	V				225°		

A5. Check your answers to part (b) by calculating the x- and y-components for each of the four vectors and comparing the answers to the components measured in part (a). Explain any differences.

PART B: Translating From One Representation to the Others

In this part, you will be given partial information for different vectors. Fully express each vector in all three representations. Be sure to indicate the scale used to draw the directed line segment for each vector.

B1. One morning, a group of hikers travels 10km East and 5km South. Express their displacement in all three representations.

B2. A block slides down a rough incline with an acceleration of $2m/s^2$. Express its acceleration in all three representations using the xy coordinate system shown in the diagram.

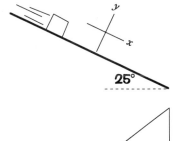

B3. A marble rolls up an incline as shown with an initial speed of 80cm/s and slowing down at a rate of $4m/s^2$.

    (a) Express the initial velocity of the marble in all three representations.

    (b) Express the acceleration of the marble in all three representations.

Be sure to indicate the scale and the coordinate system you used to answer this question.

B4. A cannon ball is fired at an angle of 30° from the vertical as shown. Ten seconds later it is observed to land 290m away, so we can estimate the horizontal component of the initial velocity to be about –30m/s. Express the initial velocity of the cannon ball in all three representations.

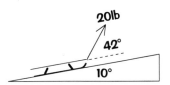

B5. A sled is pulled up a shallow, 10° hill at an angle of 42° relative to the hill as shown, with a force of 20lb. Express this force in all three representations.

B6. A baseball player throws a ball to another player with an initial speed of 20m/s and an x-component of –15m/s. Express this velocity in all three representations.

B7. A model rocket experiences a drag force of 150N @ 250°.

    (a) Express this force in all three representations.

    (b) Estimate the direction angle for the rocket's velocity. Explain how you made this estimate.

Reflection

R1. Why do we use different representations of vectors, instead of choosing one and using it exclusively? Is any particular representation easiest for describing a vector to someone else? Which one?

R2. Assume that you are given the direction of a vector and one of its components. Describe a procedure for finding the other component.

R3. Assume you are given the magnitude of a vector and one of its components. Can you uniquely determine the other component? Explain. What additional information would help you determine the other component?

Adding Vectors

Purpose and Expected Outcome

Upon completing this activity, you will be able to add two or more vectors together using either components or directed line segments.

Prior Experience / Knowledge Needed

You should be familiar with the three major representations of vectors (as a directed line segment, as a set of components, and as a magnitude and a direction). You should be able to draw a directed line segment given either components or a magnitude & direction. Also, you should be able to translate back and forth between components and magnitude & direction.

ADDING VECTORS USING DIRECTED LINE SEGMENTS

Consider two consecutive displacements: from point 1 to point 2 (displacement vector **A**) and from point 2 to point 3 (displacement vector **B**). First, draw vector **A**; then draw vector **B**. The vector sum of **A** and **B** is displacement vector **R**, which starts at point 1 and ends at point 3.

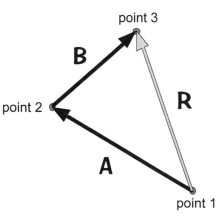

We can use the same procedure to define vector addition for all other vector quantities, such as velocity and force. To add two vectors, simply draw the first one, then draw the second such that its tail is located at the same point as the head of the first. The resultant vector is the directed line segment that goes from the tail of the first to the head of the second.

To add more than two vectors together, just continue the process, always putting the tail of each vector at the head of the previous one. An example is shown below. The resultant vector **R** is equal to **A + B + C + D + E**.

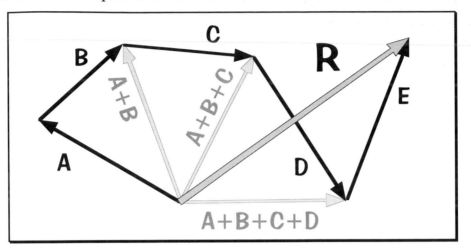

The resultant vector does not depend upon the order in which the vectors are added. For example, in the diagram below, you can see that **A + B + C** is equal to **C + B + A**, as well as **B + C + A**.

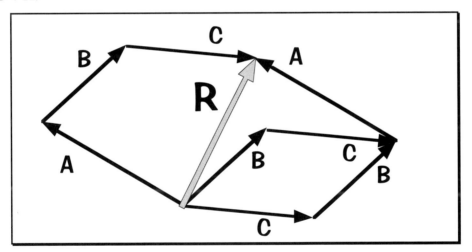

Explanation of Activity

PART A: Adding Vectors Using Directed Line Segments

For each situation below, draw directed line segments to represent each of the individual vectors mentioned in the description, and draw the resultant vector. You will need a ruler and a protractor to measure distances and angles. When you are finished, specify the resultant vector as a magnitude and a direction.

A1. On the first day of their trip, a group of hikers walked 8 miles to the Northeast. On the second day, they traveled 10 miles West. On the third day, they walked 12 miles Northwest. What was the net displacement of the hikers from the beginning of the first day to the end of the last day?

A2. Gary is trying to cross a river which flows North to South at 8km/h. Gary swims directly West (relative to the river) at 2km/h. To find Gary's velocity as seen from the banks of the river, add these two velocity vectors. What is Gary's velocity?

A3. In the middle of the same river as A2, Gary starts to swim Northward at 2km/h. What is his velocity relative to the banks?

A4. At a certain instant while shooting a basketball, Pam applies a force of 10N at an angle of 50° relative to the horizontal. The earth applies a force of about 2N directed straight downward. To find the net force on the basketball at this instant, add these two forces. What is the net force on the basketball?

A5. A glider is being towed by a small airplane. The tow rope pulls with a force of 1500N at an angle of 20°. The air (with a combination of lift and air resistance) pushes with a force of 500N at an angle of 140°. The earth pulls on the glider with a force of 500N. What is the net force on the glider?

Additional Background

ADDING VECTORS USING COMPONENTS

The addition of vectors using directed line segments is straightforward, but inconvenient, especially if a mathematical representation is desired. The best way to add vectors mathematically is to use components to <u>calculate</u> (rather than measure) the resultant vector. To see why this always works, let's go back to our example of adding vectors **A** and **B**.

We have re-drawn the original diagram for the addition of vectors, with dashed lines to indicate the components of **A**, **B**, and the resultant **R**:

Keeping in mind that A_x and R_x are <u>negative</u>, we can write:

$$R_x = A_x + B_x$$
$$R_y = A_y + B_y$$

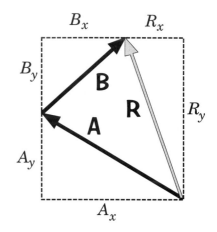

This is actually a completely general result. Given any set of vectors, we can find the components of their sum by adding the components of the individual vectors. For example, the sum of the vectors (8, 7), (6, –5), (–4, –3), and (–2, 1) is shown below, first graphically using directed line segments, then mathematically, using components:

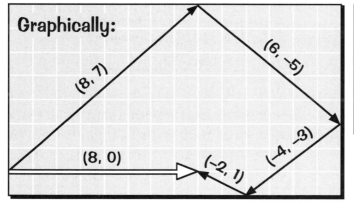

Graphically:

(8, 7) (6, –5) (8, 0) (–2, 1) (–4, –3)

Mathematically:

(8, 7) + (6, –5) + (–4, –3) + (–2, 1)

= (8 + 6 – 4 – 2, 7 – 5 – 3 + 1)

= (8, 0)

PART B: Adding Vectors Using Components

In this part, you will answer a variety of questions using components of vectors. In some cases, you must work backwards from the components of the resultant vector to find one or more components. Each answer should be given both as a set of components and as a magnitude and a direction.

B1. On the first day of their trip, a group of hikers walked 8 miles to the Northeast. On the second day, they traveled 10 miles West. On the third day, they walked 12 miles Northwest. What was their net displacement during the three days?

B2. Gary is trying to cross a river which flows North to South at 8km/h. Gary swims directly West (relative to the river) at 2km/h. What is his actual velocity (as seen by someone standing on the bank of the river)?

B3. A cannon fires a cannonball at a speed of 40m/s at 30° above the horizontal. The cannon is put onto a railroad car and is fired when the car is maintained at a constant speed of 20m/s on horizontal tracks. If the cannon is fired as shown, what is the resultant velocity of the cannonball as it leaves the cannon as seen by someone standing beside the tracks? (**Hint:** The vertical component of the resultant velocity is +20m/s.)

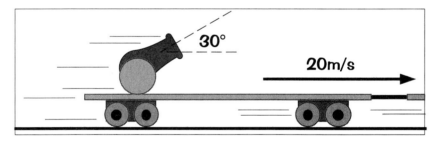

B4. A wagon is being pulled by a rope along a horizontal surface with a force of 4N at an angle of 70°. The earth pulls downward with a force of 16N, and the ground pushes straight up with an unknown force. Assuming that the net force points to the right, find (a) the net force, and (b) the force of the ground. (**Hint:** The vertical component of the force exerted by the rope is +3.8N.)

Reflection

R1. Find two non-zero vectors for which the sum of their magnitudes is equal to the magnitude of their vector sum.

R2. Find two non-zero vectors for which the sum of their direction angles is equal to the direction angle of their vector sum.

R3. Compare your answers to questions 1 and 2 in parts A and B (that is, compare A1 to B1 and A2 to B2). Did you get the same results in part B as you did in part A? Explain any differences.

R4. Describe the procedure you used to find the force of the ground in question B4.

R5. Was your answer to question B4 close to what you expected? Explain any differences between what you expected and what you found.

Finding Changes in Vector Quantities

Purpose and Expected Outcome

In this activity, you will learn how to determine the change in a vector quantity, such as position or velocity. After finishing this activity, you will be able to use either directed line segments or components to calculate average velocity (as a change in position divided by time) or average acceleration (as a change in velocity divided by time).

Prior Experience / Knowledge Needed

You should be comfortable with the three major representations of vectors, and you should be able to convert from any one of them to both of the others. Also, you should know how to add two or more vectors using both directed line segments and components.

FINDING THE CHANGE IN A VECTOR QUANTITY

We have already defined the change in position as the displacement, so you actually already know how to find the change in a vector quantity, even though you might not realize it! Imagine two points in an xy-plane. These positions are represented by the directed line segments $\mathbf{r}_1$ and $\mathbf{r}_2$ in the diagram at right. We know that the displacement $\Delta\mathbf{r}$ is a vector that goes <u>from</u> point 1 <u>to</u> point 2. So, one

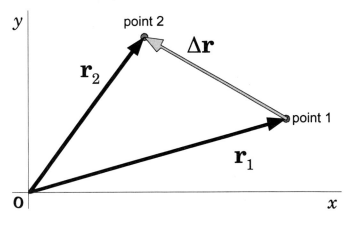

way to find the change in a vector quantity is to put them tail to tail, and to draw a directed line segment from the head of one to the head of the other. We represent this as: $\Delta\mathbf{r} = \mathbf{r}_2 - \mathbf{r}_1$.

Another way to think of the change in a vector quantity is by adding the negative:

$$\Delta \mathbf{r} = \mathbf{r}_2 - \mathbf{r}_1 = \mathbf{r}_2 + (-\mathbf{r}_1)$$

But what is the negative of a vector?

The negative of a vector is a vector of the same magnitude but pointing in the opposite direction. (Note that the sum of a vector and its negative is always zero!) The change in position is now represented using vector addition as follows, with the same result:

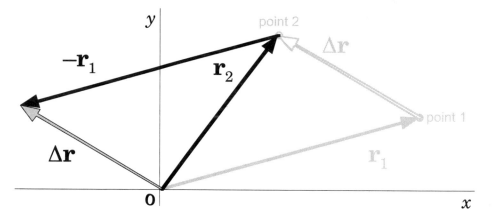

A <u>third</u> way to find the difference between two vectors is to use components. If

$$\mathbf{r}_1 = (x_1, y_1)$$
$$- \text{ and } -$$
$$\mathbf{r}_2 = (x_2, y_2),$$

then:

$$\Delta \mathbf{r} = \mathbf{r}_2 - \mathbf{r}_1 = (x_2 - x_1, y_2 - y_1).$$

All three of these methods are valid for finding the difference between any two vectors. For example, when calculating the average acceleration for a process, we need to first calculate the change in velocity and then divide by the duration of the time interval. Let's say that at $t = 0\text{s}$, an object is moving at 60m/s @ 40° above the horizontal, and at $t = 8\text{s}$, the same object is moving at 60m/s @ 40° below the horizontal (see diagram). The average acceleration during this 8s time interval is:

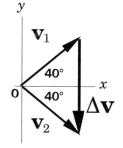

$$\mathbf{a}_{\text{ave}} = \frac{\Delta \mathbf{v}}{\Delta t} = \frac{\mathbf{v}_2 - \mathbf{v}_1}{t_2 - t_1} \approx \frac{(46, -39)\text{m/s} - (46, 39)\text{m/s}}{8\text{s} - 0\text{s}} = \frac{(0, -78)\text{m/s}}{8\text{s}}$$

$$\mathbf{a}_{\text{ave}} \approx (0, -9.8)\text{m/s}^2$$

Note that we have converted the initial and final velocities to components in order to calculate the change in velocity.

Explanation of Activity

We now return to King's Court to answer some more questions about different people's movements around town. Use both components and directed line segments to answer each question about average acceleration. Use a ruler and protractor as needed.

Example. Jerome runs along Main and Jump Streets from the Grocery Store to the Fire Station in 4 minutes, running at the same speed the whole way.

(a) How far does Jerome run?

Answer: s = total distance = 847m

Explanation: From the Grocery Store to Town Hall is 400m. From Town Hall to the Fire Station is a vector having components 200m East and 400m North, so the total distance is $400m + \sqrt{(200m)^2 + (400m)^2} = 847.2m$

(b) How fast does he run?

Answer: $v = 3.53m/s$

Explanation: Average speed is total distance divided by total time.

(c) What are his velocities while on Main Street and on Jump Street?

Answer: $\mathbf{v}_1 = 3.53m/s$ @ $180° = (-3.53, 0)m/s$ (on Main Street)
$\mathbf{v}_2 = 3.53m/s$ @ $63.4° = (1.58, 3.16)m/s$ (on Jump Street)

Explanation: He runs at constant speed, so his average speed is his speed at any given time. On Main Street, he is running West. On Jump Street, he is running 63.4° North of East.

(d) If it takes Jerome 1.6s to turn the corner at Town Hall, what is his average acceleration during this time interval?

Answer: $\mathbf{a}_{ave} = (3.19, 1.97)m/s^2 = 3.75m/s^2$ @ $31.7°$ N of E
Explanation: The average acceleration is the change in velocity divided by the duration of the time interval. $\Delta\mathbf{v} = \mathbf{v}_2 - \mathbf{v}_1 = (5.11, 3.16)m/s$, and $\Delta t = 1.6s$. This can be seen graphically below:

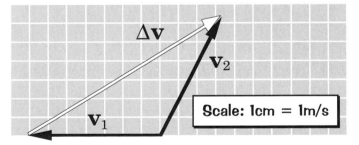

We measure $\Delta\mathbf{v}$ to be 6.1m/s @ 31°, and then calculate $\mathbf{a}_{ave}$ to be 3.8m/s² @ 31°.

continued

A1. Heather rides a bus from her house to the Key Store by way of Sixth Avenue. While on Sixth Avenue, the bus goes 60km/h, and to turn onto Baseline Drive, it slows down to 15km/h. If it takes 3s to slow down and make the turn, what is the average acceleration of the bus? (Give your answer in m/s².)

A2. A fire truck leaves the Fire Station to go to Town Hall. As it turns left onto Jump Street, the truck makes a 90° turn in 1.2s, and goes from 8km/h to 12km/h.

(a) What is the truck's velocity just before it starts to turn onto Jump Street?

(b) What is the truck's velocity just as it finishes its turn onto Jump Street?

(c) What is the truck's average acceleration while it is turning?

A3. Gary was driving his car up Sixth Avenue toward the Magic Shop when he collided with another car traveling West on Main Street. Gary was going about 18m/s, and the other car was going about 20m/s, when the collision occurred. The two cars were in contact for about 0.2s, and Gary was traveling at about 16m/s directly away from the Key Store after the collision. What was Gary's average acceleration during the collision?

Reflection and Integration

R1. Describe the method you prefer to find the difference between two vectors.

R2. Is the direction of the change in velocity during a certain time interval always the same as the direction of the average acceleration during the same time interval? Explain.

R3. Imagine an object traveling in a circle at constant speed. At the instant shown, the object is moving to the right with speed v. Consider an instant just before and an instant just after the one shown. Draw the velocity of the object at each of these times. What is the difference between these two vectors? What direction does it point? What direction does the average acceleration point? What can you say about the direction of the acceleration of the object at the time shown?

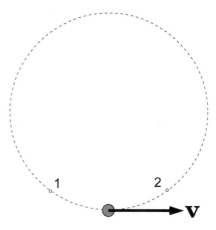

Recognizing Interactions

Purpose and Expected Outcome

In this activity you will learn to recognize when two objects are interacting and when they are not.

Prior Experience / Knowledge Needed

When two objects influence each other we say that they are *interacting*. The effect of an interaction can vary depending on the circumstances. Sometimes the motions of the objects are changed in some way. (Ultimately this is what we will be most interested in understanding.) At other times the shapes of one or more objects are changed, such as when a spring is compressed. Quite often both the motion and the shape of objects are affected by an interaction, although sometimes we can ignore the effects because they are so small.

Explanation of Activity

There are three parts to consider in this activity. In the first part, you are asked to specify whether or not particular pairs of objects are interacting and how they influence each other. In the second part, you will examine the interaction during specified periods of time. In the third set, you will explore the influence of an interaction on the environment in which the object exists.

PART A: Recognizing the Interaction between Two Objects

For each of the situations described below in A1 – A3, (a) indicate if the pair of objects specified are interacting, and (b) indicate how each object influences the other. (For example, is the shape, or motion, or both affected?) Then, answer the questions below about the situations.

A1. A water balloon is set on a spring one meter off the ground. Consider the water balloon and the spring.

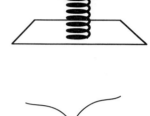

    (a) Are the water balloon and the spring interacting?

    (b) How does each influence the other?

A2. A child stands on a wooden plank joining two large boulders on opposite sides of a brook. Consider the child and the plank.

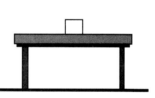

    (a) Are the child and the plank interacting with each other?

    (b) How does each influence the other?

A3. A block sits at rest on a horizontal table. Consider the block and the table.

    (a) Are the block and the table interacting?

    (b) How does each influence the other?

A4. In situation A1, if the spring were to suddenly disintegrate, what would happen to the water balloon?

A5. (a) In situation A2, is the child interacting (directly) with the boulders?

    (b) With what object is the child interacting <u>directly</u>?

A6. (a) In what ways are the spring, the plank, and the table the same?

    (b) How are they different?

PART B: Exploring an Interaction at Different Times

Consider the following situation: A baseball is thrown by the pitcher and then hit by the batter.

For each of the time periods described in B1 – B3, (a) indicate whether or not the ball and the bat are interacting, (b) indicate how the ball influences the bat, and (c) indicate how the bat influences the ball. Then answer the questions below.

B1. When the ball has left the pitcher's hand, but has not yet arrived at the batter...
- (a) Are the ball and the bat interacting?
- (b) How does the ball influence the bat?
- (c) How does the bat influence the ball?

B2. When the ball is in contact with the bat (for only about 0.002 seconds!!)...
- (a) Are the ball and the bat interacting?
- (b) How does the ball influence the bat?
- (c) How does the bat influence the ball?

B3. When the ball is in the air and heading straight toward the left fielder...
- (a) Are the ball and the bat interacting?
- (b) How does the ball influence the bat?
- (c) How does the bat influence the ball?

B4. Do the bat and ball need to be in contact to interact with each other? Explain.

B5. Give some examples of pairs of objects that interact <u>without</u> being in contact with each other?

PART C: Exploring an Interaction in Different Situations

Consider two magnets. When opposite poles are facing each other, the two magnets stick to each other as shown to the right:

C1. Each magnet is connected to a spring, which in turn is attached firmly to a wall. The magnets are placed with opposite poles facing each other, and released. All surfaces are frictionless.

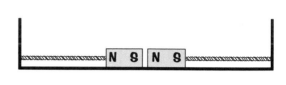

(a) Are the two magnets interacting? Explain.

(b) Describe how the magnets influence each other.

C2. Each magnet is connected to a piece of string, which is attached firmly to a wall. The magnets are placed with opposite poles facing each other, and released. All surfaces are frictionless.

(a) Are the two magnets interacting? Explain.

(b) Describe how the magnets influence each other.

C3. One magnet is connected to a spring, which is attached to the ceiling. The second magnet is placed on the floor with opposite poles facing each other.

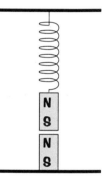

(a) Are the two magnets interacting? Explain.

(b) Describe how the two magnets influence each other.

Reflection

R1. When an object interacts with another object is there anything other than its shape and motion that could be affected? Explain.

R2. When two objects interact, must they influence each other in exactly the same way? Explain.

R3. Is it possible for one object to influence another object's interactions with a third object? Explain.

R4. Comment on the similarities and differences between a string and a spring.

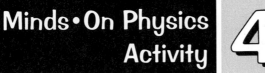

Identifying Interactions

Purpose and Expected Outcome

In this activity you will learn to identify the interactions between objects and to describe their effects.

Prior Experience / Knowledge Needed

When two objects influence each other we say that they are *interacting*. The effect of an interaction can vary depending on the circumstances. Sometimes the motions of the objects are changed in some way. (Ultimately this is what we will be most interested in understanding.) At other times the shapes of one or more objects are changed, such as when a spring is compressed. Quite often both the motion and the shape of objects are affected by an interaction, although sometimes we can ignore the effects because they are so small.

Explanation of Activity

There are three parts to this activity. In the first part, you will explore situations in which there are exactly two interactions with a certain object. In the second part, each object interacts with three other agents. In the third part, each object interacts with an unspecified number of agents.

PART A: Exploring Situations Having Two Interactions

For each of the situations below, there are exactly two interactions between the specified object and its environment. (a) Indicate the 2 *agents* that interact with the object. Then, (b) describe how the situation would change if the effect of each agent could be removed, and (c) indicate if the object is accelerating.

A1. A feather falls to the ground.

    (a) What are the two agents interacting with the feather?

    (b) <u>For each agent</u>, how would the behavior of the feather be different if its effect was removed? (**Hint:** Without one of the agents, the feather would accelerate at about 9.8m/s^2.)

    (c) Is the feather accelerating? Explain your answer.

A2. A rock is released from rest, 1 meter above the earth.

    (a) What are the two agents interacting with the rock?

    (b) <u>For each agent</u>, how would the behavior of the rock be different if its effect was removed? (**Hint:** Without one of the agents, the rock would not move; it would remain at rest.)

    (c) Is the rock accelerating? Explain your answer.

A3. A skydiver has reached terminal velocity.

    (a) What are the two agents interacting with the skydiver?

    (b) <u>For each agent</u>, how would the behavior of the skydiver be different if its effect was removed?

    (c) Is the skydiver accelerating? Explain your answer.

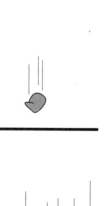

PART B: Exploring Situations Having Three Interactions

For each of the situations below, there are exactly three interactions between the specified object and its environment. (a) Indicate the 3 agents that interact with the object. Then, (b) describe how the situation would change if the effect of each agent could be removed, and (c) indicate if the object is accelerating.

B1. A balloon is filled with helium gas and attached to the ground.

(a) What are the three agents interacting with the balloon?

(b) <u>For each agent</u>, how would the behavior of the balloon be different if its effect was removed?

(c) Is the balloon accelerating? Explain your answer.

B2. A skydiver falls to the earth with her parachute opened.

(a) What are the three agents interacting with the skydiver?

(b) <u>For each agent</u>, how would the behavior of the skydiver be different if its effect was removed?

(c) Is the skydiver accelerating? Explain your answer.

B3. A ball is swung in a horizontal circle at constant speed.

(a) What are the three agents interacting with the ball?

(b) <u>For each agent</u>, how would the behavior of the ball be different if its effect was removed?

(c) Is the ball accelerating? Explain your answer.

PART C: Identifying All Possible Interactions

For each of the situations below, (a) list all the agents that interact with the specified object. Then, (b) describe how the situation would change if the effect of each agent could be removed, and (c) indicate if the object is accelerating.

C1. The space shuttle moves away from the launch pad just after take-off.

(a) What are the agents interacting with the space shuttle?

(b) <u>For each agent</u>, how would the behavior of the space shuttle be different if its effect was removed?

(c) Is the space shuttle accelerating? Explain your answer.

C2. A book slides across the floor before coming to rest after 2m.

(a) What are the agents interacting with the book?

(b) <u>For each agent</u>, how would the behavior of the book be different if its effect was removed?

(c) Is the book accelerating? Explain your answer.

C3. A coffee mug sits on a table with a giant dictionary on top of it.

(a) What are the agents interacting with the coffee mug?

(b) <u>For each agent</u>, how would the behavior of the coffee mug be different if its effect was removed?

(c) Is the coffee mug accelerating? Explain your answer.

Reflection

R1. Under what conditions is air an important agent? (That is, under what conditions must we include interactions of an object with the air surrounding it?)

R2. Under what conditions can we ignore the effects of the air surrounding an object? (For example, can we ignore the effects of air when something is traveling very fast?)

R3. Does a string stretch when you pull on it? Why or why not?

Interpreting Measurements of Forces

Purpose and Expected Outcome

A spring scale is often used to measure the magnitude of a force being exerted on an object. Unfortunately, to understand the meaning of a given measurement (or a set of measurements) requires some understanding of the forces that are exerted. It is nearly impossible to give a general, unambiguous procedure for measuring forces. The purpose of this activity is to help you bring to light some of the things we tend to assume are true (and are not necessarily so) when we use a spring scale to measure forces. After completing this activity you should have some appreciation of the difficulties involved in developing procedures for determining force laws. You will also have a better sense of the limitations of spring scales for determining the magnitude of a force exerted on an object.

Prior Experience / Knowledge Needed

You should have some familiarity with identifying the interactions that are present in a physical situation.

You should have available the following equipment:

- several simple and equivalent spring scales;
- a platform scale;
- a set of blocks or other objects having different masses;
- a small pulley; and
- some light string or fishing-line.

Explanation of Activity

This activity consists of four parts, each having several cases. In each case you are asked to create a physical arrangement of spring scales and blocks. Then you will record your scale readings and analyze the situations.

PART A: What Is Being Measured?

Arrange your apparatus as shown and answer the questions below.

A1. An object hangs vertically from a spring scale as shown.
  (a) What is the reading of the spring scale?
  (b) What force (or combinations of forces) is the spring scale measuring?
  (c) Identify the objects exerting these forces.

A2. A hand pushes up gently on the hanging object as shown.
  (a) What is the reading of the spring scale?
  (b) What force (or combinations of forces) is the spring scale measuring?
  (c) Identify the objects exerting these forces.

A3. Someone pulls down on the hanging object as shown.
  (a) What is the reading of the spring scale?
  (b) What force (or combinations of forces) is the spring scale measuring?
  (c) Identify the objects exerting these forces.

PART B: Are Your Scales Equivalent?

(This part may be skipped if your scales are known to be equivalent.)

Use tape to label each of your three scales (A, B & C) and two blocks (I & II). Then arrange your apparatus as shown, fill in the table, and answer the questions below.

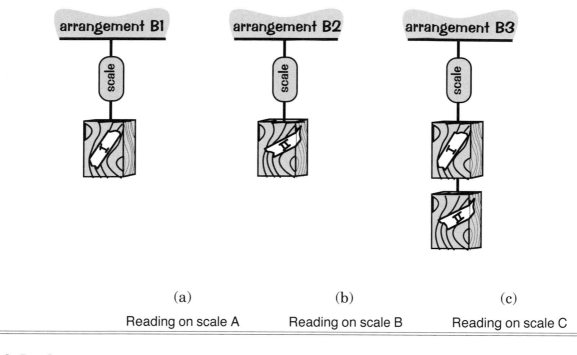

	(a)	(b)	(c)
	Reading on scale A	Reading on scale B	Reading on scale C

B1. Block I only.

B2. Block II only.

B3. Blocks I & II.

B4. Are your scales equivalent to each other? Describe any discrepancies. How would you compensate for discrepancies?

B5. How did the scale readings change when you added the second block? Is this what you expected? Explain.

B6. What would you expect the readings to be if you added a third block?

PART C: How Does Force Vary with Location in a Vertical Chain?

In the following, it is assumed that all your scales are equivalent. If they are not equivalent, you must first determine how to make compatible measurements with your spring scales. (Compatible measurements are measurements that can be compared to one another.) Arrange your apparatus as shown to the right, fill in the table with the readings on your three scales, and answer the questions below.

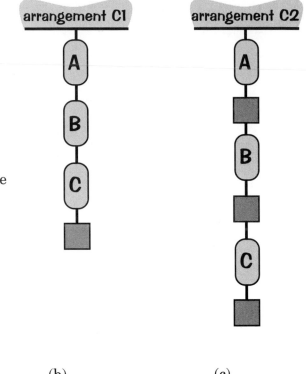

	(a)	(b)	(c)
	Reading on scale A	Reading on scale B	Reading on scale C

C1. 3 scales in a row; 1 block hanging from the bottom.

C2. 3 scales in a row; 1 block hanging from each scale.

C3. How do the scale readings change with location in the vertical chain?

C4. Is this what you expected? Explain.

C5. Explain why the scales read the values that they do.

PART D: How Does the Scale Reading Depend Upon Location and Orientation?

In the following, it is again assumed that all of your scales are equivalent. Arrange your apparatus as shown, then fill in the table with the readings on your scales, and answer the questions below.

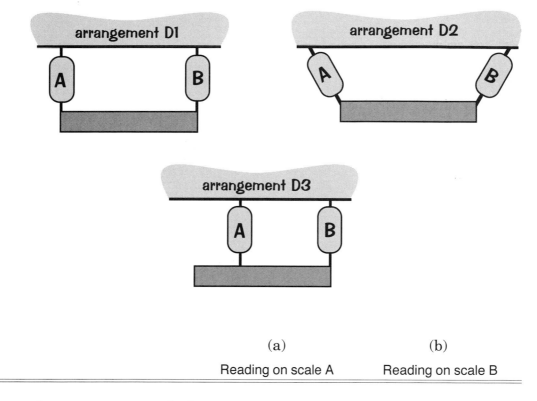

	(a) Reading on scale A	(b) Reading on scale B
D1. Vertical springs; one attached at each end of the bar.		
D2. Tilted springs; one attached at each end of the bar.		
D3. Vertical springs; one shifted from the end of the bar.		

D4. How do the readings change with the placement and orientation of the spring scales?

D5. Is this what you expected? Explain.

D6. Explain the variation in scale readings.

Integration of Ideas

Consider the arrangement at right. <u>Before setting it up</u>, predict the readings of each of the three spring scales. Then, construct the arrangement and determine if your predictions are correct. Explain any discrepancies.

	Reading on scale A	Reading on scale B	Reading on scale C

I1. Predictions:

I2. Measurements:

I3. Do your predictions match up with your measurements? Explain any differences.

Reflection

R1. Can using a spring scale to measure the force(s) exerted on an object change the magnitude of the force(s)? Give an example.

R2. If a spring scale changes the magnitude of the force(s) being exerted on an object is the spring scale actually measuring what it was intended to measure? Explain.

R3. If more than one spring scale is used to make a measurement can you always get the magnitude of the force (or the combination of forces) exerted on an object by simply adding up the readings on the two spring scales? Explain.

R4. To hold a spring scale in place while it is being used to make a measurement, you need to exert a force on the other end. How does this force affect the measurement made by the spring scale?

44

More Interpreting Measurements of Forces

Purpose and Expected Outcome

This activity is a continuation of the previous activity, in which we began to explore the difficulties in measuring forces and in understanding what exactly we are measuring. At the end of this activity you should understand better how different forces act on particular objects in static and dynamic situations.

Prior Experience / Knowledge Needed

You should have experience with spring scales and platform scales. You should be able to recognize when something is interacting directly with a particular object (as opposed to indirectly through one or more direct agents).

You should have available the following equipment:

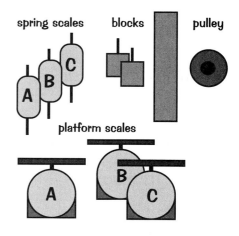

- several simple and equivalent spring scales;
- several equivalent platform scales;
- a set of blocks or other objects having different masses;
- a small pulley; and
- some light string or fishing-line.

Explanation of Activity

In this activity, you will explore additional situations in which more than one force is exerted on particular objects. You will also explore a situation in which the objects are accelerating.

PART A: Scale Readings with Multiple Platform Scales

Arrange your platform scales as shown, fill in the table with the readings on all of the scales, and answer the questions below.

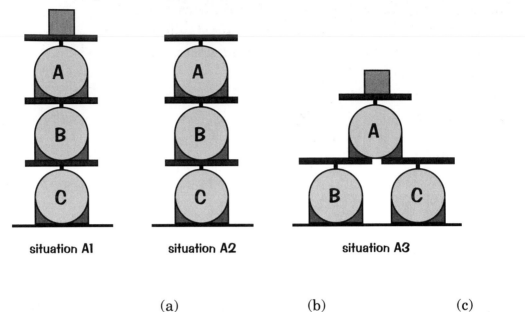

situation A1   situation A2   situation A3

	(a) Reading on scale A	(b) Reading on scale B	(c) Reading on scale C
A1. 3 scales in a row; 1 block on top.			
A2. 3 scales in a row; no block on top.			
A3. 2 scales side-by-side, with one scale partially on both and a block on top of everything.			

A4. How does the reading in A1(b) compare to the sum of the readings in A3(b) and A3(c)? Explain.

A5. What is the weight of a typical platform scale? How many of the readings above did you use to make this estimate?

A6. For each of the three arrangements, explain the reading on scale C.

PART B: Scale Readings with Multiple Forces

Arrange your apparatus as shown to the right. This is arrangement B1. Arrangements B2 and B3 are the same, except that there are 2, then 3, blocks hanging from the right-hand side of the pulley. For each arrangement, fill in the table with the readings on all of the scales, and answer the questions below.

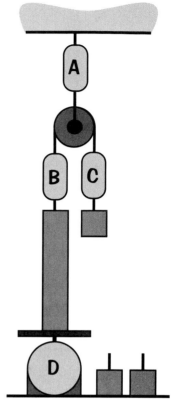

	(a) Reading on scale A	(b) Reading on scale B	(c) Reading on scale C	(d) Reading on scale D
B1. 1 block hanging from scale C.				
B2. 2 blocks hanging from scale C.				
B3. 3 blocks hanging from scale C.				

B4–6. For each reading above, make a table indicating what force or combination of forces is being measured by that particular scale.

	(a) Forces measured by scale A	(b) Forces measured by scale B	(c) Forces measured by scale C	(d) Forces measured by scale D
B4. 1 block hanging from scale C.				
B5. 2 blocks hanging from scale C.				
B6. 3 blocks hanging from scale C.				

B7. How are the different scale readings related to each other?

PART C: Scale Readings with an Accelerating System

Arrange your apparatus as shown. This is arrangement C1. Arrangements C2 and C3 are the same, except that there are 2, then 3, blocks hanging from scale C. Unlike all the earlier arrangements, this one will move when you let go of it! So make sure you set it up such that you have enough time to read the readings on (at least) one of the scales. You should repeat the motion many times with each arrangement to make sure you get each of the three readings as accurately as you can. Make a table of readings, then indicate what force or combination of forces is being measured on each scale and explain (in question C7) how the readings are related to each other.

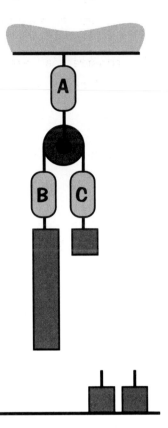

	(a) Reading on scale A	(b) Reading on scale B	(c) Reading on scale C
C1. 1 block hanging from scale C.			
C2. 2 blocks hanging from scale C.			
C3. 3 blocks hanging from scale C.			

	(a) Forces measured by scale A	(b) Forces measured by scale B	(c) Forces measured by scale C
C4. 1 block hanging from scale C.			
C5. 2 blocks hanging from scale C.			
C6. 3 blocks hanging from scale C.			

C7. How are the different scale readings related to each other?

Integration of Ideas

Below we present a series of puzzles, a set of challenges. The general theme is "How would you measure the weight [of something]..." under certain conditions and constraints. For each puzzle, specify your answer either in words or with a diagram (or preferably both!).

I1. You would like to measure the weight of an object that is heavier than the maximum reading on any of your scales. A rough estimate (just by holding it yourself) is that the object weighs less than twice the maximum reading of your scales. How would you measure its weight?

I2. Suppose now that you have only one scale with which to measure the weight of this object. How would you weigh it in this case?

I3. What if you have an object that is much heavier than the maximum reading of any of your scales? How would you measure its weight?

Reflection

R1. A single spring scale is connected to a single object. Is the scale reading equal to the weight of the object? Explain. (Give examples if possible.)

R2. An object hangs from two spring scales and is in contact with nothing else. Under what conditions is the sum of the scale readings equal to the weight of the object? Give at least two examples for which the sum of the readings is <u>not</u> equal to the weight.

R3. (a) An object weighing 2lbs is hanging from a single spring scale. What does the scale read?

　　　(b) Now imagine dropping the arrangement. What would the scale read in this case? Explain.

R4. Compare your scale readings for scales A and C in parts B and C. (For example, compare reading B1(a) to reading C1(a).) Which scale readings were the same in both parts? Which ones were different? Explain.

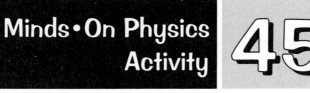

Recognizing Forces in Realistic Situations

Purpose and Expected Outcome

This activity will familiarize you with several common forces. After completing this activity, you should be able to: (a) discuss the behavior of the forces of gravitation, spring, tension, normal, friction, buoyancy, and air resistance; and (b) decide whether a particular force is present in a given situation.

Prior Experience / Knowledge Needed

You should already have some experience with interactions and with how to measure force. When two objects *interact*, each exerts a *force* on the other. Below, we describe nine common forces. You should read these descriptions before beginning this activity, then refer to the table as needed during the activity. You do <u>not</u> need to have a complete understanding of these forces before you begin. Your understanding of the forces will expand and improve as you work through and discuss the activity.

As you read the descriptions of the nine forces, keep in mind that physics deals with many forces that are not on this list. However, the forces described here are sufficient to understand and analyze many common situations.

TABLE OF COMMON FORCES

Force	Short description of force	When is this force present?
Normal	The force that one object exerts on another by pushing on it. The direction is directly away from the surface that exerts the force.	Whenever two objects are touching.
Tension	The force that a string, cable, cord or rope exerts on an object by pulling on it. The direction is always parallel to the string and away from the object being pulled.	Whenever a string is attached and is *taut* (rather than *slack*).
Spring (or Elastic)	The force exerted by a spring that is stretched or compressed. Stretched springs pull; compressed springs push.	Whenever a spring is attached and is either compressed or stretched from its relaxed state.
Buoyant	The force that a fluid (such as water or air) exerts on an object it is touching. The buoyant force is always exerted opposite the direction of the local gravitational field.	Whenever an object is partially or fully immersed in a fluid, and both are in a gravitational field.
Friction *(static)*	The force that one object exerts on another to prevent it from sliding across it. The direction is parallel to the surfaces in contact.	Whenever there is a non-zero normal force <u>and</u> when the objects would slide without the force.
(kinetic)	The force that objects exert on each other when they are sliding across each other. The direction is opposite the relative motion of the two objects.	Whenever there is a non-zero normal force and a non-zero coefficient of kinetic friction.
Air Resistance	The force that air (or another gas) exerts to oppose the motion of an object moving relative to it. The direction is opposite the relative motion of the object and the air.	Whenever an object moves through the air, or when there is a wind.
Gravitational	The attractive forces that objects exert on each other due to their masses. The direction is along a line connecting their centers.	Whenever two objects both have non-zero mass.
Electric	The forces that objects exert on each other due to their electric charges. The direction is along a line connecting their centers. Opposite charges attract; like charges repel.	Whenever two objects both have a non-zero electric charge.
Magnetic	The forces that magnetic poles exert on each other. Opposite poles attract; like poles repel.	Magnets exert magnetic forces on one another and on certain materials (such as iron) that behave like magnets in their presence.

Explanation of Activity

In the pages that follow, we describe several situations. For each problem situation, indicate which forces are exerted on the given object and state what features of the situation you used to determine the presence of each force. Then indicate the object that exerts each force as well as the general direction of the force. (For now, consider <u>only</u> the forces of Gravitation, Spring, Tension, Normal, Buoyancy, Friction, and Air Resistance.)

Example. A block rests on an inclined plane without sliding.

Answers:

FORCE	FEATURE	WHAT EXERTS FORCE?	DIRECTION OF FORCE
Gravitation	*The block has mass.*	*earth*	*toward earth*
*Gravitation**	*The block has mass.*	*incline*	*toward incline*
Normal	*The block is in contact with another object.*	*incline*	*directly away from the surface*
*Buoyancy**	*The block is immersed in a fluid.*	*air*	*upward*
Static Friction	*The block is at rest.*	*incline*	*up incline, parallel to the surface*

* can usually be neglected because it is so small.

This part contains six situations. For each specified object, animal, or person, (a) list the forces exerted on it, (b) indicate the feature that you used to determine that each force is present, (c) indicate the agent that exerts each force, and (d) indicate the direction of each force.

A1. A monkey hangs <u>at rest</u> from the ceiling by a piece of rope. Consider only the forces on the <u>monkey</u>.

A2. A monkey hangs <u>at rest</u> from the ceiling by a spring. Consider only the forces on the <u>monkey</u>.

A3. A ball is shot into the air with a spring-loaded cannon. Consider the forces on the <u>ball</u> only at its highest point.

A4. A skydiver (who has not yet opened her parachute) falls at constant velocity (terminal velocity). Consider only the forces on the <u>skydiver</u>.

A5. A book sits <u>at rest</u> on top of a table. Consider only the forces on the <u>book</u>.

A6. A book <u>slides</u> across the top of a table. Consider only the forces on the <u>book</u>.

Reflection (for part A)

R1. How did you decide what forces were exerted on the objects in part A? For example, how do you know that a normal force is acting on an object? How do you know that gravity is acting?

R2. Can there be more than one tension force exerted on an object? How would you recognize such a situation? Give an example of a situation in which there are two tension forces exerted on something.

Summary of Part A

Here is a way of determining if any of these seven forces is exerted on an object.

- If the object is near the earth (or any other massive object) and the object has mass, there is a force of gravity. The direction is always toward the other object.

- For each spring attached to the object, *as long as the spring is either stretched or compressed*, there is a spring force. The direction is toward the unstretched state.

- For each string attached, *as long as the string is not slack*, there is a tension force. Strings always pull.

- For each surface in contact with the object, there is a normal force, which points perpendicularly away from the surface, and a friction force, which points parallel to the surface and opposes the <u>relative</u> motion of the two objects.

- If the object is moving in air (or other gas), or if there is a wind, there is a force of air resistance. The direction of this force is the same as the direction of the air's relative velocity.

- If the object is immersed in a fluid, and both are in a gravitational field, there is a force of buoyancy. The direction is opposite the direction of the local gravitational field.

Now use this system to help you complete part B.

PART B

This part contains three situations. For each specified object, (a) list the forces exerted on it, (b) indicate the feature that you used to determine that each force is present, (c) indicate the agent that exerts each force, and (d) indicate the direction of each force.

B1. A book <u>slides</u> across the top of a table. Consider only the forces on the <u>table</u>.

B2. A coffee mug sits <u>at rest</u> on a table with a huge dictionary on top of it. Consider only the forces on the <u>coffee mug</u>.

B3. A ball is thrown into the air toward a wall. Consider the forces on the <u>ball</u> only when it is touching the wall.

Integration of Ideas

Use the diagram below to answer all the questions in this part. All objects are at rest. All springs are stretched from their relaxed state. All strings are massless.

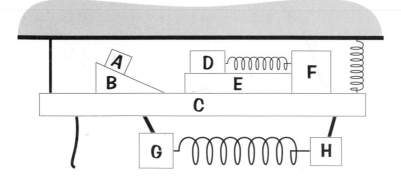

I1. Which objects have at least two normal forces exerted on them?

I2. Which objects have the most normal forces exerted on them? How many normal forces are there?

I3. Which object has a tension force exerted on it with a direction angle of about 75°?

I4. Which objects have a horizontal normal force exerted on them?

I5. Which objects have more than one force of gravity due to the earth exerted on them?

I6. How many tension forces are exerted on object C?

I7. Which objects <u>must</u> have a friction force exerted on them?

Reflection (continued)

R3. Which of the objects (in parts A and B) may have had a non-zero acceleration? Why is it that these objects accelerate and the others do not?

R4. The forces discussed in this activity are the seven most common ones in introductory physics. What other forces have you heard of? Do any of them behave like the ones considered here? Which ones? Explain.

Comparing Magnitudes of Common Forces

Purpose and Expected Outcome

In this activity you will explore several common forces in more detail. After completing this activity, you should be able to decide what factors determine the magnitude of a particular force.

Prior Experience / Knowledge Needed

You should be familiar with the following three forces: Gravitational, Spring, and Tension.

Explanation of Activity and Example

This activity consists of three parts, one part for each of three common forces. For each force, a variety of situations is presented, and you are asked to compare selected pairs of situations. For each pair, select the situation in which the force has the larger <u>magnitude</u>. If the force has the same magnitude in both situations, say so. If you do not have enough information to determine which force has the larger magnitude, say so. In each case, briefly explain your answer.

PART A: Comparing Magnitudes of the Spring Force

In each situation, consider the force that the spring exerts on the block attached to it. All the springs are identical. L is the natural (relaxed) length of the spring; d is some particular distance (the same in each situation). The blocks in A, B, C, E, and F all have the same mass, while the block in D has a larger mass, and the block in G has a smaller mass (than the blocks in A, B, C, E and F).

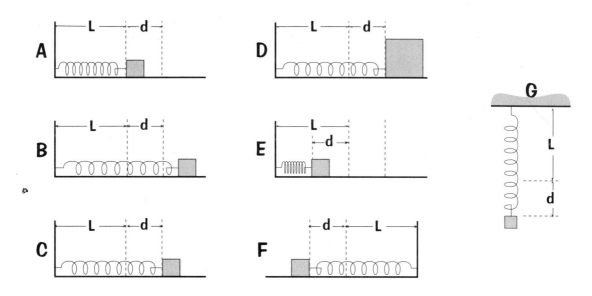

> **Example.** In which situation is the <u>magnitude</u> of the spring force larger, A or C? Explain.
>
> *Answer: The spring force is greater in C. The greater the distance a spring is stretched or compressed from its relaxed state, the greater the magnitude of the spring force. In situation A, the spring force is zero, because the spring is neither compressed nor stretched.*

A1. In which situation is the <u>magnitude</u> of the spring force larger, B or C? Explain.

A2. C or D? Explain.

A3. C or E? Explain.

A4. C or F? Explain.

A5. C or G? Explain.

PART B: Comparing Magnitudes of the Gravitational Force

In each situation, consider the gravitational force <u>that the earth exerts on the block</u>. The masses of the blocks in situations A, C, D, E, F and G are the same. The mass of the block in situation B is four times that of the block in situation A, and the masses of the blocks in situations H and I are each twice the mass of the block in situation A.

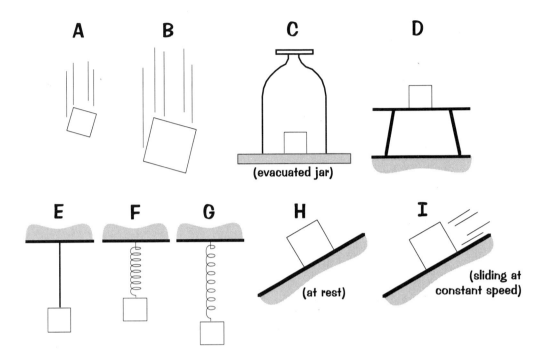

B1. In which situation is the <u>magnitude</u> of the gravitational force larger, A or B? Explain.

B2. A or C? Explain.

B3. A or D? Explain.

B4. A or E? Explain.

B5. E or F? Explain.

B6. F or G? Explain.

B7. A or H? Explain.

B8. E or H? Explain.

B9. H or I? Explain.

PART C: Comparing Magnitudes of the Tension Force

In each situation, consider the tension force <u>that the string exerts on the block</u>. If there is more than one string attached to the block, consider the one indicated by the arrow. All the blocks have the same mass.

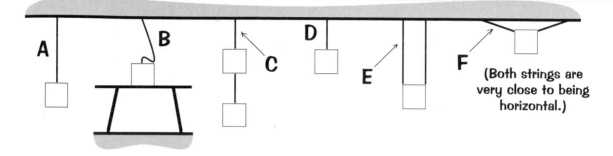

C1. In which situation is the <u>magnitude</u> of the tension force larger, A or B? Explain.

C2. A or C? Explain.

C3. A or D? Explain.

C4. A or E? Explain.

C5. A or F? Explain.

C6. E or F? Explain.

Reflection

R1. What factors determine the magnitude of the gravitational force?

R2. What factors determine the magnitude of the spring force?

R3. What factors determine the magnitude of the tension force? How is the tension force different from the gravitational and spring forces?

R4. (a) Imagine hanging an object from a rope, and then hanging it from a spring. Is there any difference between a very stiff spring and a rope? Comment on the similarities.

    (b) Is there any difference between a moderately stiff spring and a very stretchy rope? Comment on the similarities.

More Comparing Magnitudes of Common Forces

Purpose and Expected Outcome

This activity is a continuation of the previous activity. In this activity you will explore several common forces in more detail. After completing this activity, you should be able to decide what factors determine the magnitude of a particular force.

Prior Experience / Knowledge Needed

You should be familiar with the following three forces: Normal, Friction, and Air Resistance.

Explanation of Activity

This activity consists of three parts, one part for each of three common forces. For each force, a variety of situations is presented, and you are asked to compare selected pairs of situations. For each pair, select the situation in which the force has a larger <u>magnitude</u>. If the force has the same magnitude in both situations, say so. If you do not have enough information to determine which force has the larger magnitude, say so. In each case, briefly explain your answer. An example can be found in part A of Activity 46.

PART A: Comparing Magnitudes of the Normal Force

In each situation, consider the normal force <u>that the table or incline exerts on the block in contact with it</u>. The <u>white</u> blocks in A, C, D, E, F, G, and H all have the same mass. The block in situation B has 8 times the mass of the block in situation A. The small, dark block in situation C has one-half the mass of the block underneath it.

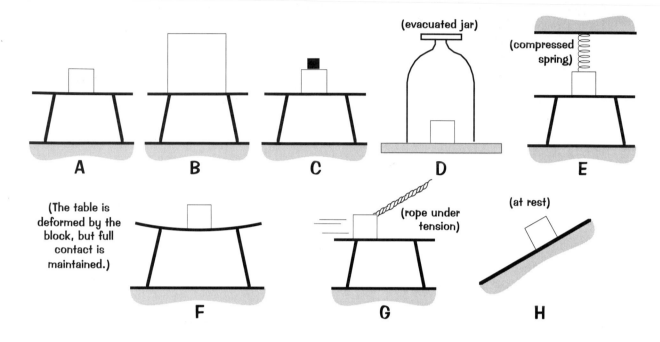

A1. In which situation is the <u>magnitude</u> of the normal force larger, A or B? Explain.

A2. A or C? Explain.

A3. A or D? Explain.

A4. A or E? Explain.

A5. A or F? Explain.

A6. A or G? Explain.

A7. A or H? Explain.

PART B: Comparing Magnitudes of the Kinetic Friction Force

In each of the following situations, consider the kinetic (sliding) friction force <u>that the surface exerts on the block in contact with it</u>. All the situations have the same coefficient of kinetic friction. The masses of the blocks are the same in A, B, D, E, and F. The mass of the block in C is 4 times the mass of the other blocks. The block in B is moving twice as fast as the other blocks. The block in D has twice the area in contact with the surface as the block in A.

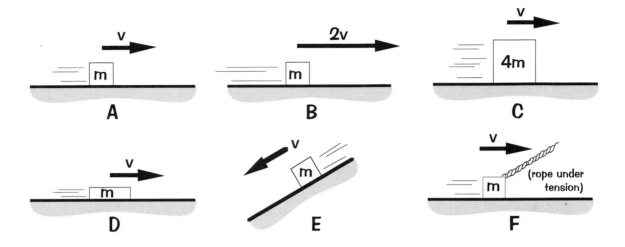

B1. In which situation is the <u>magnitude</u> of the kinetic friction force larger, A or B? Explain.

B2. A or C? Explain.

B3. A or D? Explain.

B4. A or E? Explain.

B5. A or F? Explain.

B6. B or C? Explain.

B7. C or E? Explain.

PART C: Comparing Magnitudes of the Force of Air Resistance

In each of these situations, consider the force <u>on the car due to air resistance</u>. The masses of the cars in A, B, C, D, and E are all the same. The car in F is the same size and shape as the others, but its mass is twice the mass of the others. Car B is moving twice as fast as the others. For situation E, consider the total force of air resistance on <u>the car and the drag chute</u>. The shape parameter is the same for all 6 cars.

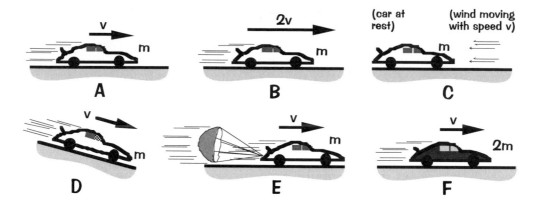

C1. In which situation is the <u>magnitude</u> of the air resistance force larger, A or B? Explain.

C2. A or C? Explain.

C3. A or D? Explain.

C4. A or E? Explain.

C5. A or F? Explain.

Reflection

R1. Consider the six forces you have studied in the last two activities. For which of these six forces does the magnitude of the force exerted on an object depend upon the other forces exerted on the object? Give an example for each type of force. How do you explain why the magnitude of these forces appears to depend upon other forces?

R2. Describe a situation in which the normal force exerted on an object is larger than the gravitational force on the same object.

R3. Describe a situation in which the tension force exerted on an object is larger than the gravitational force on the same object.

Understanding
Friction Forces

Purpose and Expected Outcome

At the end of this activity you should understand better the differences and similarities between static and kinetic (sliding) friction forces.

Prior Experience / Knowledge Needed

FRICTION FORCES

Loosely speaking, the interaction called *friction* inhibits two objects from sliding across one another. Friction is termed *static* if the interaction <u>completely</u> prevents the two surfaces from sliding across one another, and they act as though they are stuck together. (That is, they have the <u>same</u> velocity.) Friction is termed *sliding* or *kinetic* if the two objects slide across one another. This occurs whenever two objects are touching, but they have <u>different</u> velocities.

Friction occurs at the *interface* where two surfaces touch each other. A friction force is exerted on each of the objects whose surfaces are in contact. For kinetic friction, the direction of the force depends upon the <u>relative</u> motion of the two objects. For example, imagine that a coin is sitting on an empty seat in a car. When the car speeds up, the coin starts to move backwards (as seen from the inside of the car), and the friction force points forward. In fact, the coin is also moving forward (as seen from the ground), and so the friction force is in the same direction as the motion of the coin! In general, the direction of the kinetic friction force on an object is opposite to the motion of the object <u>as seen from the object touching it</u>.

For static friction, the direction of the force depends on the situation. Unlike kinetic friction, the magnitude and direction of the static friction force cannot, generally, be determined without using Newton's laws.

Explanation of Activity and Example

In the first part of this activity, you will determine which type of friction acts where two surfaces meet. In the second activity, you will also determine the direction in which the friction force is exerted. You do not need to know how large or small the friction force is to determine which type it is or what the direction is.

PART A: Identifying Friction Forces by Type

In each of the following situations, one or more pairs of surfaces in contact is indicated. For each pair of surfaces, indicate whether the force of friction experienced by the objects is static or kinetic. Then give a short explanation for your choice.

Example. A block slides down an inclined plane.

Answer: Kinetic. The friction is kinetic because the block <u>slides</u> over the surface of the incline.

A1. A block is attached to a horizontal string under tension.

   (a) The block is <u>at rest</u>.

   (b) The block <u>moves to the right</u>.

A2. Two blocks slide down an inclined plane...

   (a) at different speeds.

   (b) at the same speed.

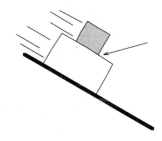

A3. A bicycle is on a hill.

   (a) The bike travels down the hill with its <u>brakes on</u>. The tires <u>roll without slipping</u> on the road. (Consider both interfaces.)

   (b) The bike is <u>stationary</u>. (Consider both interfaces.)

#1 (between brake and tire)

#2

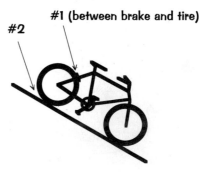

continued

A4. One block is stacked on top of another block as shown. A horizontal string under tension is attached to the upper block. (Consider both interfaces for each part.)

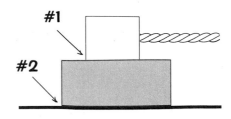

(a) Both blocks move to the right with the <u>same speed</u>.

(b) Both blocks move to the right with <u>different, non-zero speeds</u>.

(c) The upper block moves to the right, while the lower block remains at rest.

A5. A car is on a horizontal road.

(a) The car is <u>moving</u>, while the tires <u>roll without slipping</u>.

(b) The car remains <u>at rest</u>, while the tires are <u>spinning</u>.

(c) The car is <u>moving</u>, but skidding to a halt with the tires <u>not spinning</u>.

A6. A child is sitting on a spinning merry-go-round.

(a) The child spins in a circle of constant radius. (Consider the interface between the child and the merry-go-round.)

(b) The child holds a penny in her hand. (Consider the interface between the penny and the hand.)

(c) The child puts the penny on the surface of the merry-go-round, and it flies off. (Consider the time period when the penny is touching the surface, and consider the interface between the penny and the surface.)

PART B: Determining the Direction of Kinetic Friction

For each object in each situation, determine the type of friction force exerted on it due to each surface it touches. For kinetic friction only, give the direction of the friction force.

	Situation		Special Conditions	Surface to Consider	Type of Friction	Direction of Force
B1.	One block is stacked on top of another block as shown. A rope <u>under tension</u> is attached to the lower block. Both blocks move to the right.	(a)	Blocks A and B move at the same speed.	1. bottom of A 2. top of B 3. bottom of B		
		(b)	Block A moves faster than B.	1. bottom of A 2. top of B 3. bottom of B		
		(c)	Block A moves slower than B.	1. bottom of A 2. top of B 3. bottom of B		
B2.	Two blocks are attached to the same piece of string as shown. A rope <u>under tension</u> is attached to the lower block.	(a)	A and B are <u>at rest</u>. The string is <u>slack</u>.	1. bottom of A 2. top of B 3. bottom of B		
		(b)	A and B are <u>at rest</u>. The string is <u>taut</u>.	1. bottom of A 2. top of B 3. bottom of B		
		(c)	A and B move at the <u>same speed</u>. Block B moves to the right.	1. bottom of A 2. top of B 3. bottom of B		
B3.	A ladder is sliding down a wall as shown.		The upper-right end of the ladder stays in contact with the wall at all times, and the other end stays in contact with the floor at all times.	(a) Upper-right end of the ladder (b) Lower-left end of the ladder.		

continued

B4. A cup is on a table that is covered by a tablecloth. The tablecloth is pulled to the right. | The cup is observed to move slower than the tablecloth. | bottom of the cup

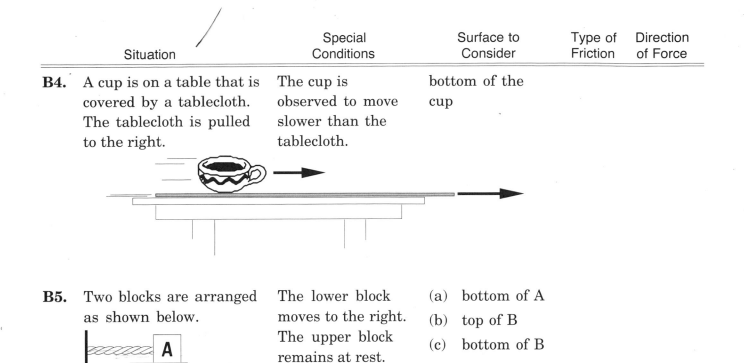

B5. Two blocks are arranged as shown below. | The lower block moves to the right. The upper block remains at rest. | (a) bottom of A
 (b) top of B
 (c) bottom of B

Reflection

R1. If an object is at rest, can the friction force exerted on it ever be kinetic? Explain, preferably with examples.

R2. If an object is moving, can the friction force exerted on it ever be static? Explain, using examples.

R3. (a) Consider two friction forces that are the result of contact between two blocks, A and B. The first friction force is exerted <u>on</u> A <u>by</u> B, and the second is exerted <u>on</u> B <u>by</u> A. If the first friction force is static, can the second one ever be kinetic? Explain.

(b) How are the directions of these two force vectors related? Explain.

R4. Many of the objects in this activity are in contact with tables and other objects that remain at rest. (For example, consider the table in question B4, and block A in question B5.) How can they remain at rest when the objects touching them are applying friction forces? Why do they not move? Explain.

When drawing a free-body diagram it is customary to draw a <u>point</u> to represent the body. This point should be drawn <u>away</u> from any other illustration or diagram. In a free-body diagram the object is drawn as a point because Newton's laws are valid only for point objects. On this drawing, show each force exerted on the body as a directed line segment with the tail end of the vector starting at the point. The direction of the arrow should be in the same direction as the force. Whenever possible the length of the vector should be drawn to be roughly proportional to the size of the force. Each force in the diagram should be <u>clearly labeled</u> and distinguishable from all the other forces present in the physical situation.

When the diagram is to be used to help write the dynamical law, $\mathbf{F}_{net} = m\mathbf{a}$ in component form, a set of axes, indicating the component directions, should be drawn on the free-body diagram. These axes can be placed anywhere on the diagram but are often placed with the origin located at the point representing the center of the object. Also, these axes can be oriented in any way. Usually, the orientation is chosen to make it easier or more convenient to find components of the forces.

Sometimes, for illustration purposes, the object is drawn as having spatial extent, such as a block or square, with all the forces drawn from a point at the center of the body. When drawing the object it is important to preserve the object's orientation.

Some valid free-body diagrams are shown below. Note that: (1) <u>only</u> forces appear in the diagrams (and the net force should <u>never</u> appear); (2) a coordinate system <u>may</u> be shown; and (3) whether or not the body is represented for illustration, all forces begin at a <u>point</u>.

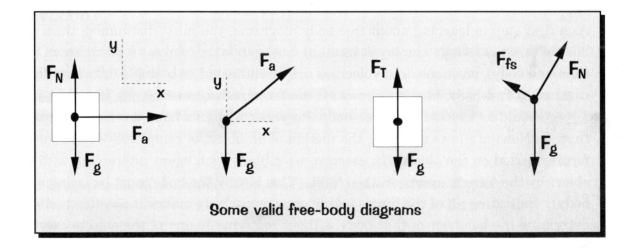

Some valid free-body diagrams

Explanation of Activity and Examples

There are two parts to this activity. In the first part, you will see if you can distinguish between valid and invalid free-body diagrams that are given to you. Then in the second part you will label given free-body diagrams with the appropriate symbols to represent the forces acting on particular objects.

PART A: Recognizing Valid Free-Body Diagrams

Presented below are descriptions of physical situations together with a diagram. For each case, (a) state whether or not the diagram is a valid free-body diagram. (b) If the diagram is not a valid free-body diagram, identify what makes the diagram invalid and give your reasons. **Note:** <u>In all cases, ignore the effects of air resistance and buoyancy.</u>

E1. A block slides along a frictionless horizontal surface with a constant velocity in the positive x-direction.

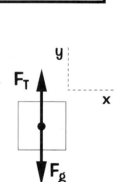

Answer: No, this diagram is not a valid free-body diagram, because the velocity is indicated. Only forces should appear on a free-body diagram.

A1. A block is suspended from a massless rope.

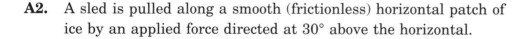

A2. A sled is pulled along a smooth (frictionless) horizontal patch of ice by an applied force directed at 30° above the horizontal.

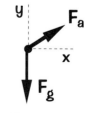

continued

A3. A book rests on a table.

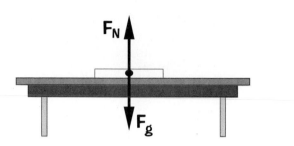

A4. An applied force $\mathbf{F}_a$ pushes a box up a smooth incline. The applied force is exerted parallel to the incline.

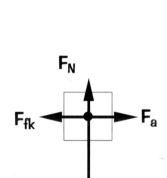

A5. A block is pulled with constant velocity along a horizontal surface having coefficient of kinetic friction μ_k.

A6. A wagon is pulled along the floor at an angle of 30° above the horizontal. Ignore frictional effects.

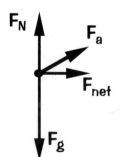

PART B: Interpreting Free-Body Diagrams

Free-body diagrams contain a lot of information. Much (but not all) of the information is contained in the presence, relative size, and orientation of each of the forces shown on the diagram.

A number of physical situations are described below, together with an illustration of each situation and a valid, but unlabeled, free-body diagram for each object in the situation. For each force in each free-body diagram, identify its nature (e.g., friction or normal) and source (e.g., the table). Ignore air resistance and buoyancy.

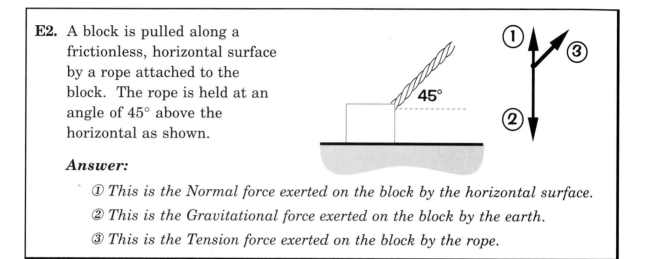

E2. A block is pulled along a frictionless, horizontal surface by a rope attached to the block. The rope is held at an angle of 45° above the horizontal as shown.

Answer:

   ① *This is the Normal force exerted on the block by the horizontal surface.*

   ② *This is the Gravitational force exerted on the block by the earth.*

   ③ *This is the Tension force exerted on the block by the rope.*

B1. A mass *M* hangs at rest from a vertical spring.

B2. A 10kg block is pushed as shown at a constant speed *v* along a rough, horizontal surface.

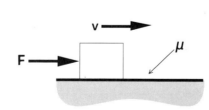

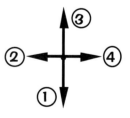

continued

B3. A block having mass m_1 sits at rest on a horizontal surface. A second block m_2 sits on top of the first block.

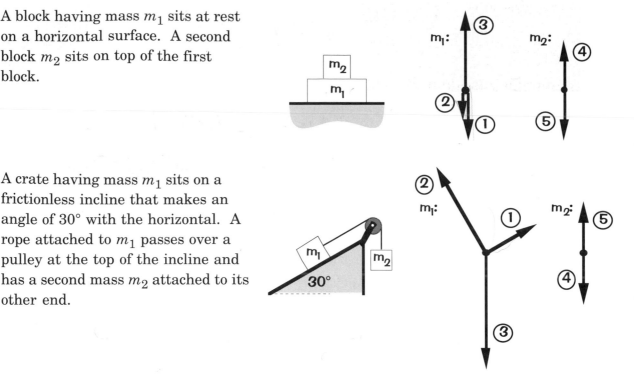

B4. A crate having mass m_1 sits on a frictionless incline that makes an angle of 30° with the horizontal. A rope attached to m_1 passes over a pulley at the top of the incline and has a second mass m_2 attached to its other end.

Reflection

R1. Fill in each blank space below with the appropriate word or phrase:

There are five features common to all free-body diagrams.

(a) _____ are the only vector quantities that appear in free-body diagrams; velocities, accelerations, etc. are never included. In particular, _____ force should never appear in a free-body diagram.

(b) _____ forces exerted on a particular object are present in the free-body diagram for the object.

(c) Each force is clearly _____ .

(d) _____ _____ object is considered in a free-body diagram.

(e) All forces start at a single _____ .

There are also two optional features of free-body diagrams.

(f) A _____ _____ may be indicated on the free-body diagram. The orientation is chosen to make finding components easier or more convenient. The placement may be either directly on the center of the diagram or off to the side.

(g) A _____ of the object on which the forces are exerted may be drawn on the free-body diagram, provided its orientation in the drawing is the same as its physical orientation. However, the other objects it is _____ with should never be drawn on the free-body diagram.

R2. How would you represent the forces present in a physical situation when there are two or more objects to consider?

Drawing and Using
Free-Body Diagrams

Purpose and Expected Outcome

After completing this activity, you should be able to draw valid free-body diagrams. Also, you should be able to use free-body diagrams to write expressions for the components of the net force.

Prior Experience / Knowledge Needed

You should be familiar with the idea that force is a vector quantity. You should be able to recognize a valid free-body diagram, and you should know what belongs, and what does <u>not</u> belong, in a valid free-body diagram.

Explanation of Activity and Examples

This activity consists of three parts. In the first part, you will draw valid free-body diagrams for blocks in a variety of situations. In the second part, you will draw some free-body diagrams and use them to find components of vectors. In the third part, you will be given valid free-body diagrams for different objects. For each object, you will use its free-body diagram to find the components of all of the forces exerted on it, and then you will write out a mathematical expression for the net force acting on the object.

PART A: Drawing Free-Body Diagrams

For each block in each situation, draw and label a valid free-body diagram to describe the forces acting on it. (**Note:** You should ignore the forces of air resistance and buoyancy in this activity.)

E1. A block of mass m is supported from the ceiling by two ropes as shown.

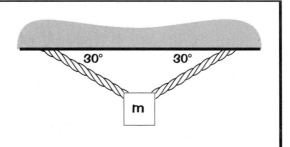

Answer:

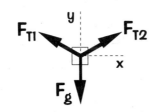

Explanation: *There are two ropes, so there are two tension forces, labeled F_{T1} and F_{T2}. The force of gravitation points straight down.*

Note: *There are many ways to draw the free-body diagram for this object: The sketch of the block and/or the coordinate system may be missing, or the coordinate system may be moved to one side.*

A1. A block of mass m is suspended from the ceiling by a light string.

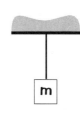

A2. A block having mass m is pulled by a horizontal force $\mathbf{F}_a$ in the positive x-direction along a rough, horizontal surface.

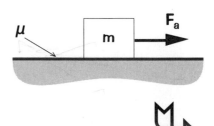

continued

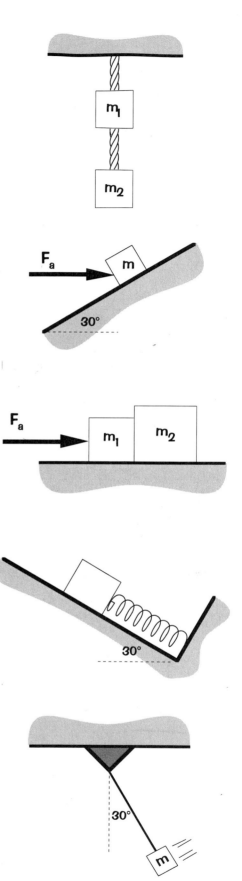

A3. A block of mass m_1 is suspended from the ceiling by a rope. Attached to the bottom of m_1 is a second rope, from which a second mass, m_2, hangs.

A4. A 100kg block is pushed up a smooth (frictionless) ramp by a horizontal force, $F_a = 2000N$. The ramp makes an angle of 30° relative to the horizontal.

A5. Two blocks, having masses $m_1 = 5$kg and $m_2 = 10$kg, are in contact and sit side-by-side on a smooth, horizontal surface. A force F_a directed to the right is applied to m_1 and both blocks accelerate with $a = 2$m/s^2.

A6. A 5kg block is at rest on a smooth ramp that makes an angle of 30° with the horizontal. The block is supported by a spring placed at the bottom of the ramp.

A7. A block of mass m is attached to a string and released from rest when the string is horizontal. (Draw the free-body diagram for the block at the instant shown.)

PART B: Finding Components of Forces

There are two situations to consider in this part.

B1. A metal ball is at rest on a metal channel as shown below.

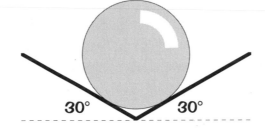

(a) Draw a free-body diagram for the metal ball.

(b) Write expressions for the horizontal and vertical components of the force exerted by the <u>right-hand</u> side of the channel.

(c) Write expressions for the horizontal and vertical components of the gravitational force exerted by the earth.

B2. Two blocks of wood are attached to opposite ends of a piece of string and arranged on a frictionless wedge as shown.

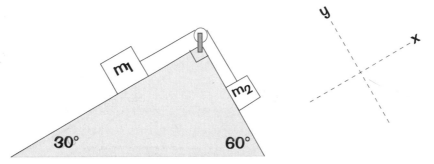

(a) Draw a free-body diagram for each of the blocks of wood.

(b) Using the coordinate frame above, write expressions for the x- and y-components of the force exerted by the wedge on m_1.

(c) Using the coordinate frame above, write expressions for the x- and y-components of the force exerted by the string on m_1.

(d) Using the same coordinate frame, write expressions for the x- and y-components of the gravitational force exerted by the earth on m_2.

PART C: Using Free-Body Diagrams to Find the Components of the Net Force

Free-body diagrams are very useful when writing Newton's second law in vector-component form. If coordinate (x- and y-) axes are clearly indicated and oriented on a free-body diagram, it is usually clear what the components are for each of the forces exerted on the object.

For each of the physical situations described below, a free-body diagram is provided for each object. Using the set of axes indicated in the diagram, write expressions for the x- and y-components of the net force in terms of the forces shown in the free-body diagram. (**Note:** We have ignored the effects of both air resistance and buoyancy in all of these situations.)

E2. A bucket of mass m hangs at rest from a rope attached to the ceiling.

Answer:

$F_{net,x} = 0$ (*No forces have components in the x-direction.*)

$F_{net,y} = F_T - F_g$

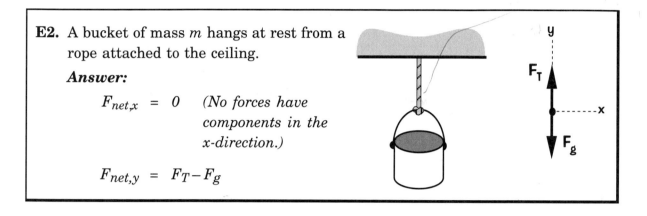

C1. A box is pulled with constant speed along a rough horizontal surface by a rope that makes an angle of 25° with the horizontal as shown.

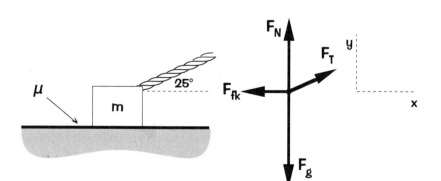

continued

C2. A box of mass M slides down a frictionless incline that makes an angle of 15° with the horizontal.

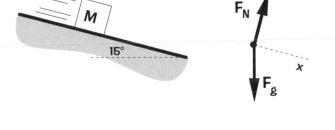

C3. A crate having mass M is pushed up a smooth 20° ramp by a horizontal force $F = 200\text{N}$.

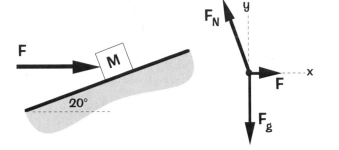

C4. A crate of mass M is pushed up a <u>rough</u> 20° incline by a horizontal force of 300N.

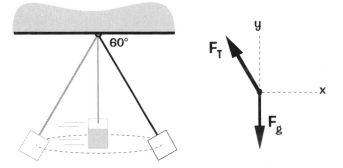

C5. A 2kg block swings in a horizontal circle as shown. The string attached to the block maintains an angle of 60° with the ceiling at all times. As seen from above, the block is moving clockwise. (The free-body diagram is drawn for the instant the block is at its rightmost point.)

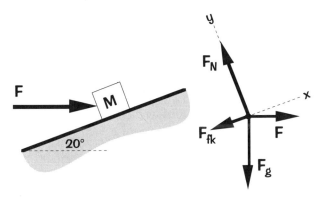

Summary

How are the forces in a free-body diagram related to the net force exerted on an object?

The net force is the vector sum of all the external forces exerted on the object, and therefore, it should never appear in a free-body diagram. After all, it is in essence already there!

How can I make my free-body diagrams as useful as possible?

First of all, you should make sure that the directions of all your forces are accurately drawn. This will help you find the components of the forces, which will help you find the net force, and ultimately, the acceleration of the object.

Then, if the sizes of the force vectors are also drawn accurately, often we can identify the direction of the net force $\mathbf{F}_{net}$. By Newton's second law, an object will always accelerate in the same direction as $\mathbf{F}_{net}$. Therefore, the net force implied by your free-body diagram should always be consistent with the magnitude and/or the direction of the object's acceleration (if either is known). For example, an object at rest or traveling with constant velocity has zero acceleration. In this instance, the vectors in your free-body diagram should add to zero, as closely as possible.

What if the acceleration of the object is non-zero?

Sometimes, we do not know the magnitude of the acceleration, particularly before we have solved the problem! Often we want to <u>solve</u> for the acceleration of an object. Even if we do not yet know the magnitude of the acceleration, sometimes we know its <u>direction</u>. For instance, if an object is sliding along a flat surface, we know that the velocity always points parallel to the surface. Therefore, all changes in velocity (as well as accelerations) also point parallel to the surface. Thus, the direction of the net force is known. Your free-body diagrams should be consistent with this fact. $\mathbf{F}_{net}$ should point parallel to the surface; there should be <u>no</u> component of $\mathbf{F}_{net}$ perpendicular to the surface.

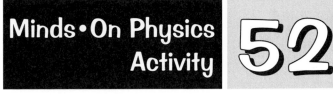

Analyzing Physical Situations Using Free-Body Diagrams

Purpose and Expected Outcome

In this activity you will learn how to use free-body diagrams (and your knowledge of vectors) to compare the magnitudes of different forces acting on a *static* object. This will help you to develop intuition about the common forces used to describe the behavior of large-scale objects.

Prior Experience / Knowledge Needed

To do this activity, you should be familiar with vector addition and vector components. Knowledge of trigonometry is helpful but not necessary; in many cases, basic principles of geometry are enough. You should be able to draw free-body diagrams accurately.

All of the situations in this activity are *static*, which means that all the objects in the situations are at rest. When an object is at rest, it is not accelerating, so the net force on it is zero. From this we can often deduce the relative magnitudes of the forces exerted on the object.

You do <u>not</u> need to know Newton's laws to do this activity.

Explanation of Activity and Examples

You will be given a variety of physical situations and will be asked to make comparisons of the forces exerted on different objects. For each object in each situation, (a) draw and label its free-body diagram, (b) answer the questions asked about the forces exerted on the objects, and (c) explain your answers.

E1. A block of mass m is hanging from the ceiling by two ropes as shown. Which is larger, the gravitational force or the tension force due to the left string?

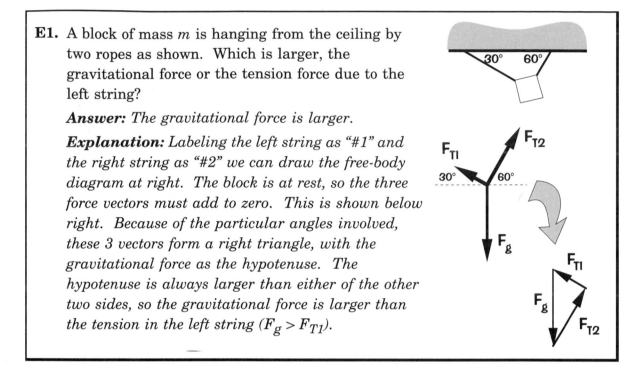

Answer: The gravitational force is larger.

Explanation: Labeling the left string as "#1" and the right string as "#2" we can draw the free-body diagram at right. The block is at rest, so the three force vectors must add to zero. This is shown below right. Because of the particular angles involved, these 3 vectors form a right triangle, with the gravitational force as the hypotenuse. The hypotenuse is always larger than either of the other two sides, so the gravitational force is larger than the tension in the left string ($F_g > F_{T1}$).

E2. A block of mass m is supported from the ceiling by two ropes as shown. Which is larger, the tension in the left string or the tension in the right string?

Answer: The tension in the right string is larger.

Explanation: Labeling the left string as "#1" and the right string as "#2" we can draw the free-body diagram at right. The block is at rest, so the net force on it must be zero. Let's focus on the x-component of the net force. Only the tension forces have x-components, as shown in gray. In order for the net force to be zero, these two components must be equal (in magnitude). As seen in the diagram, the force with the larger angle must also have the larger magnitude, so F_{T2} must be larger than F_{T1}.

Alternative Explanation: We use the free-body diagram to write out the net force in the x-direction to get:

$$F_{net,x} = F_{T2} \cos 60° - F_{T1} \cos 40° = 0$$

Because $\cos 60° < \cos 40°$, we deduce that $F_{T2} > F_{T1}$.

A1. A block of mass m is hanging from two ropes as shown.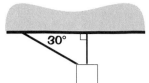

    (a) Which is larger, the gravitational force or the tension force due to the right string?

    (b) What is the tension in the left string?

A2. A 2kg block is at rest on a rough incline as shown. Which is larger, the normal force or the force of friction?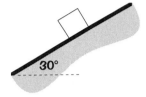

A3. A 5kg block is at rest on a smooth surface as shown.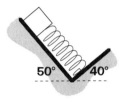

    (a) Which is larger, the spring force or the force of gravity?

    (b) Which force on the block is the smallest?

A4. A solid sphere is placed in a frictionless trough as shown. Which is larger, the normal force due to the left side of the trough or the normal force due to the right side?

A5. A solid sphere is placed in a frictionless trough as shown. Which is larger, the normal force due to the left side of the trough or the normal force due to the right side?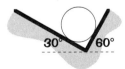

A6. Two blocks are arranged in a frictionless trough as shown. Their masses are proportional to their sizes. Of the four forces exerted on m_2, which is the smallest?

Reflection and Integration

R1. An object is attached to three strings as shown. All three strings are under tension, so there are four (non-negligible) forces exerted on the object.

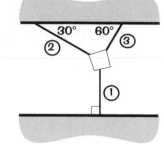

   (a) Which force is <u>always</u> larger than the tension force due to string #2? Explain.

   (b) Under what conditions is the tension in string #3 larger than the gravitational force on the object? Explain.

R2. An object is in contact with a flat surface (not necessarily horizontal). Give <u>three</u> examples in which the normal force due to this surface is larger than the gravitational force.

R3. A block is attached to two springs as shown. Which spring exerts the larger force, the left one or the right one? Explain.

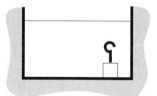

R4. A very thin wire is stretched horizontally between two walls as shown. What must be the tension in the wire so that it remains straight when a mass weighing 20N is hung from its center?

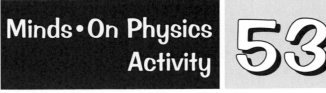

Describing Physical Situations Using Free-Body Diagrams

Purpose and Expected Outcome

In this activity, you will learn more about how to identify and recognize the forces acting on objects in different physical situations. Also, you will learn how to use free-body diagrams as a *descriptive* tool for understanding physical situations.

Prior Experience / Knowledge Needed

You should know the common forces used to describe and analyze large-scale objects, how to represent them, and how to label them. You should know how to interpret a free-body diagram.

FREE-BODY DIAGRAMS AS A DESCRIPTIVE TOOL

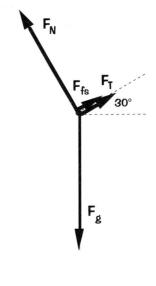

A free-body diagram is an excellent visual representation of the physical situation of an object. It contains all the force vectors that act on the object. It indicates the direction, relative size, and nature (friction, gravitational, normal, spring, or tension) of each force acting on the object. If we were given just the free-body diagram, and told nothing else about the object, we could usually determine many features of the object's environment. Consider the free-body diagram to the right. We can orient the diagram using the fact the gravitational force (F_g) always points downward. The presence of the normal force (F_N) indicates that there is something or some surface touching the object. F_N always points perpendicular to and away from the surface, and the friction force (F_{fs}) always points parallel to the surface.

continued

Thus, we know the orientation of the surface. In addition, there must be a rope (or string, or wire, etc.) attached to thé object and stretched parallel to the surface. So, the situation <u>could</u> look like this:

According to the free-body diagram, the tension force is not large enough to keep the block from sliding down the incline, so a static friction force <u>in the same direction as the tension force</u> is needed as well. However, this is not the only way in which the forces must act in this situation.

What if the tension were increased (by increasing the weight of the hanging mass)? As the tension is increased, the static friction force would become smaller and smaller, until at some point, it would become zero. This possibility is shown to the right (possibility #2). If we increase the tension some more, the static friction force would again be non-zero, except now it would point <u>down</u> the incline, since it must oppose the tension force for the block to remain at rest. This third possibility is shown at right also.

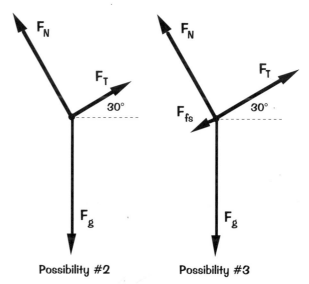

Possibility #2   Possibility #3

This is what is meant by using free-body diagrams to describe physical situations: Even though all three diagrams describe the same situation, there are different possible arrangements of forces. These possibilities arise for two reasons: (1) the <u>presence</u> of a force may be uncertain, or (2) the <u>direction</u> of a force may be uncertain. In this case, the static friction force is uncertain in both respects, and so there are three possible free-body diagrams.

Explanation of Activity and Example

In this activity, you are given 10 different free-body diagrams, labeled A through J. For each situation, (a) list every free-body diagram that could be used to describe the forces acting on the specified object, (b) explain your choices, and (c) re-draw and label each of the possible free-body diagrams.

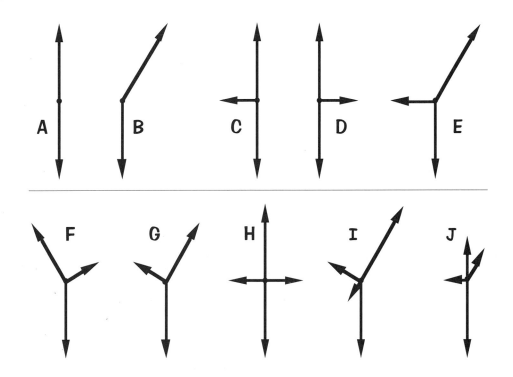

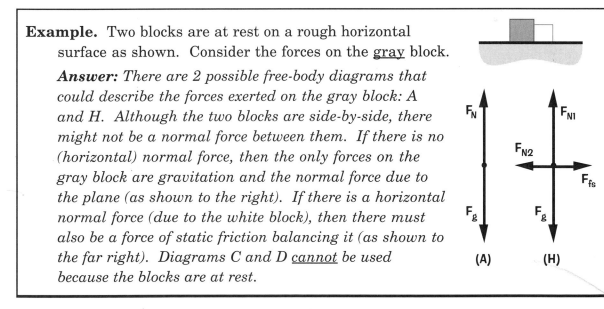

Example. Two blocks are at rest on a rough horizontal surface as shown. Consider the forces on the <u>gray</u> block.

Answer: There are 2 possible free-body diagrams that could describe the forces exerted on the gray block: A and H. Although the two blocks are side-by-side, there might not be a normal force between them. If there is no (horizontal) normal force, then the only forces on the gray block are gravitation and the normal force due to the plane (as shown to the right). If there is a horizontal normal force (due to the white block), then there must also be a force of static friction balancing it (as shown to the far right). Diagrams C and D <u>cannot</u> be used because the blocks are at rest.

continued

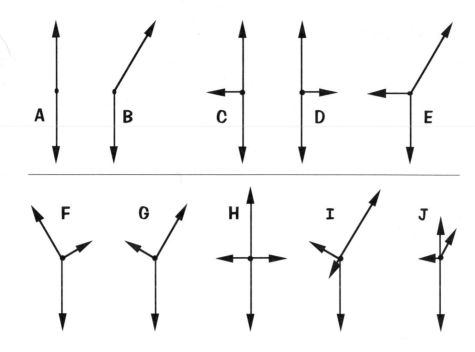

A1. A block sits at rest on a rough horizontal surface. An attached rope makes an angle of 60° with the horizontal.

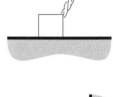

A2. A block is at rest on a rough horizontal surface as shown.

A3. A block is at rest on a rough incline having coefficient of static friction of 0.55. The incline and the rope each make an angle of 60° with the horizontal.

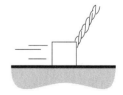

A4. A block travels to the right on a rough horizontal surface. The attached rope makes an angle of 60° with the horizontal.

A5. A block is attached to three strings as shown. The block is at rest.

Integration of Ideas

Make a table showing (a) the feature or features that indicate the possible presence of each common force; (b) the direction of the force when it is present; and (c) the conditions under which the force may be neglected, even if the features in (a) are present in the situation. (Some answers have been provided.)

FORCE	(a) FEATURE(s) that indicate possible presence of this force	(b) DIRECTION of force (if present)	(c) CONDITIONS under which force can be neglected (even if features are present)
I1. Gravitation	• The object has mass.		• No other massive objects are nearby.
I2. Tension	• A string is attached to the object.		• The string is slack.
I3. Spring			• The spring is neither compressed nor stretched from its relaxed state.
I4. Kinetic Friction	• (1) Another object is in contact; (2) the normal force is non-zero; <u>and</u> (3) objects have different velocities.	• Parallel to surface in contact; opposes <u>relative</u> motion of two objects in contact.	
I5. Static Friction		• Parallel to surface in contact; direction <u>sometimes</u> not known before full analysis.	
I6. Normal		• Directly away from surface in contact (perpendicular to surface in contact).	[**Never!** The normal force might be very small, but we always assume it's there.]
I7. Air Resistance	• (1) The object is immersed in air or other gas; <u>and</u> (2) the object is moving relative to the gas.		
I8. Buoyancy			• The object has a much larger density than the surrounding medium.

Reflection

R1. A block is at rest on a rough horizontal surface. Is there a friction force exerted on the block? Explain. If so, what direction does it point?

R2. A block is at rest on a horizontal surface with a string under tension attached. <u>Could</u> the surface be frictionless? Explain.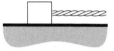

R3. Reconsider the situation in problem A2 shown to the right. (The block is at rest on a rough horizontal surface.) What can you say about the magnitude and direction of the spring force on the block? Explain.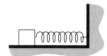

R4. Reconsider the situation in problem A5. (The block is at rest and attached to three strings as shown.) What is the range of values for the tension force due to the vertical (middle) string? Explain.

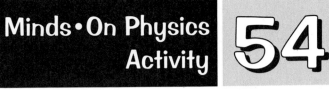
Summarizing and Structuring Interactions

Purpose and Expected Outcome

Before moving on to learn about Newton's laws, it is a good idea to organize the forces introduced so far in the course. This will make it easier for you to recall individual types of forces and to apply each correctly to problem situations. You will learn how the basic forces are different and how they are similar. You will also review the physical characteristics that affect each of the forces. Finally, you will add to your list of problem-solving ideas and practices.

Prior Experience / Knowledge Needed

You should be familiar with the Table of Forces that appears in Activity 45 (in condensed form) and in Appendix A of the Reader. You should be familiar with basic physical characteristics, such as mass, position, and speed, and how each affects different forces.

Explanation of Activity

There are three parts to this activity.

PART A: Summarizing Forces

Make a table describing all the forces you have used to understand interactions. Fill in the table as follows:

Column 1: The name of the force, such as gravitation, friction, etc.
Column 2: The symbol(s) used to represent this force in equations and in text
Column 3: A description of the force in words
Column 4: The primary agents that cause this force to be exerted
Column 5: The circumstances for which force is present and non-zero
Column 6: (If possible) how to determine its magnitude and direction

FORCE	SYMBOL(S)	DESCRIPTION	AGENTS CAUSING FORCE	CIRCUMSTANCES WHEN PRESENT	RELATIONSHIP FOR DETERMINING FORCE
⋮					
gravitation	F_g	• attraction of objects toward each other	• usually the earth	• object has mass $(m \neq 0)$	$F_g = mg$; direction is down
friction (kinetic)	...	...	⋮	• two objects with different velocities are touching	⋮
⋮					

PART B: Making Comparisons

Compare your table with the tables that other students have made. Discuss your entries and descriptions with them. Make additions and modifications to your table as needed.

PART C: Listing Problem-Solving Ideas

As a class, make a list of problem-solving ideas. These include: ways to avoid mistakes, common steps and/or procedures that can be used for different types of problems, tricks for determining a certain quantity, and general strategies for analyzing situations. Here are some examples:

- Draw a free-body diagram.
- Indicate coordinate axes on your free-body diagram.
- To determine type of friction (static or kinetic) look at the relative motion of the two surfaces in contact...
- The force of air resistance is often much smaller than other forces in a situation.

You might find it useful and helpful to review some of the Reflection questions from the last few activities.

Add this list to the one you made previously for kinematics (Activity 35).

Analyzing Physical Situations Using Newton's First and Second Laws

Purpose and Expected Outcome

In this activity, we will introduce Newton's three laws of physics, and use the first two to analyze a variety of physical situations. After finishing this activity you will be able to relate the motion of an object to the forces acting on it.

Prior Experience / Knowledge Needed

You should remind yourself of kinematics principles. For instance, how do you use a strobe diagram to recognize if and when an object is accelerating? What is the relationship between position and velocity? What is the relationship between velocity and acceleration? Is acceleration a vector or scalar quantity? What does this imply?

You should be able to interpret a strobe diagram. Also, you should be able to find components of vectors and plot those components as functions of time.

Finally, you should be familiar with the concept of force, and be able to identify the forces acting in common situations.

NEWTON'S LAWS

Sir Isaac Newton (1642–1727) published in 1686 his three laws, which relate the motion of objects (their kinematical behavior or response) to the causes of that motion (the individual forces exerted on the objects). These three laws remain the basis of how scientists view the macroscopic (large-scale) world. We sometimes refer to this view as *Classical Mechanics*.

continued

Newton's laws may be expressed as follows.

Newton's Three Laws of Motion

I. An object will remain at rest or move with constant velocity (constant speed <u>and</u> direction of motion), unless an unbalanced force is exerted on it. If so, the object has a *net force* exerted on it. (The net force is the vector sum of all the forces exerted on an object.)

II. Whenever a net force is exerted on an object, the object accelerates in the same direction as the net force. The magnitude of the acceleration is simply the magnitude of the net force divided by the mass of the object. Mathematically this is written:

$$\mathbf{F}_{net} = m\mathbf{a}.$$
(Newton's Second Law)

III. Whenever two objects interact, the force on the first due to the second is equal in magnitude and opposite in direction to the force on the second due to the first. Mathematically this is writtten:

$$\mathbf{F}_{\text{on 1, due to 2}} = -\mathbf{F}_{\text{on 2, due to 1}}.$$
(Newton's Third Law)

Sometimes we shorten this by writing simply:

$$\mathbf{F}_{12} = -\mathbf{F}_{21}$$

Explanation of Activity

This activity consists of four situations. For each situation a series of questions are asked that require you to analyze the situation using one or more of Newton's laws.

SITUATION A: Motion of a Rolling Rubber Ball

A small rubber ball rolls across the floor. For a period of time it passes over a piece of felt. After leaving the felt, it collides with a wall and rebounds, passing over the felt a second time. Assume that the motion of the ball is along a straight line path. The strobe diagram for the motion of the ball is shown below. Assume that the time interval between strobes is 0.5s.

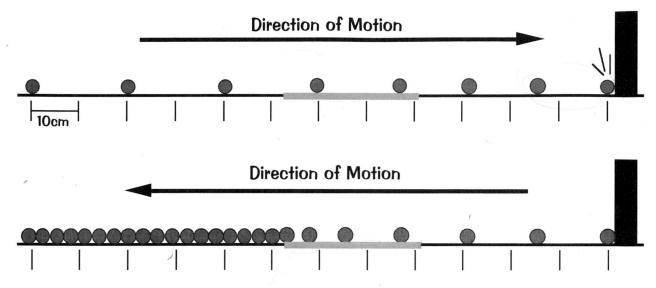

A1. Identify the forces exerted on the ball prior to reaching the felt for the first time, and indicate the agent causing each force. Is your answer consistent with Newton's first law? Explain.

A2. Use Newton's second law to determine when and where there is a net force exerted on the ball. Identify the unbalanced force for each instance.

A3. Where is the net force on the ball the greatest? Explain, using Newton's laws.

A4. For each instance that the ball is accelerating compare the direction of the net force with the direction of the acceleration.

A5. What forces are exerted on the ball the first time it travels across the felt? What forces are exerted the second time the ball travels across the felt? Compare the magnitude and direction of each force exerted while the ball is moving to the right with the corresponding force while it is moving to the left. (Which are the same in both magnitude and direction? Which are different? How are they different?)

SITUATION B: Motion of a Falling Marble

A marble is dropped from a height of 2 meters, starting from rest.
The strobe diagram for this situation is shown to the right.

B1. What forces are exerted on the marble after it is released?

B2. Which forces change as the marble falls? How do they change?

B3. After the marble is released, is there ever a time when the net force on the marble is zero? Explain.

B4. Is the acceleration of the marble ever zero? Explain.

B5. Are your answers to questions B3 and B4 consistent with Newton's second law? Explain.

SITUATION C: Motion of a Thrown Ball

A ball is thrown as shown in the strobe diagram below. At each instant the velocity of the ball is represented as a directed line segment.

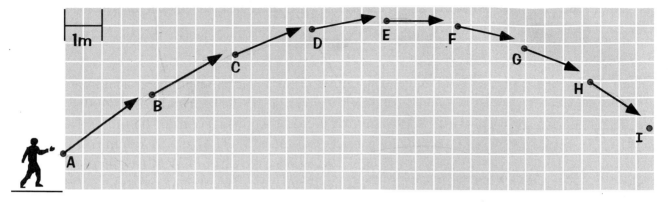

C1. A student claims that the force of air resistance is significant. Is there any evidence of this force in the diagram above? Explain your reasoning. (**Hint:** Use a sketch of x vs. t or v_x vs. t.)

C2. Draw a free-body diagram showing the forces exerted on the ball at point B.

C3. What is the direction of the net force at point E? Identify all the forces exerted on the ball at this point.

C4. What would be the acceleration of the ball at point E if there were no force of air resistance? Use Newton's second law to explain your answer.

C5. Does the thrower exert a force on the ball at point G? If so, what is the direction of the force, and how does it affect the acceleration of the ball? Explain.

SITUATION D: Motion of a Race Car

A race car moving along a two-kilometer circular track at a constant speed of 180km/h. The figure below shows the position of the car every 5 seconds during one trip around the track, with directed line segments representing the velocity at each position.

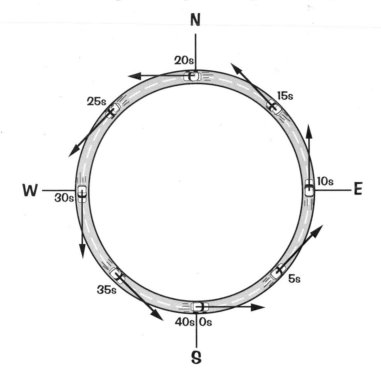

D1. Is the car accelerating at $t = 10$s (that is, is the velocity changing). If so, what is the direction of the acceleration? Explain.

D2. Draw a free body diagram for the car showing the forces exerted on the car at $t = 10$s. Indicate what object exerts each force.

D3. Which forces balance each other? Are any forces unbalanced? Which ones?

D4. Are your answers to questions D1 and D3 consistent with Newton's second law? Explain.

D5. Does the acceleration of the car change as it moves around the track? How? Do the forces change? How?

Reflection

R1. For each of the examples above was the acceleration of the object always along the direction of the net force? Explain.

R2. Can you have forces along a particular direction, yet have no acceleration? Explain. Give an example of a situation in which there is at least one force exerted in a particular direction, but the acceleration is in a different direction.

R3. Can you determine the <u>magnitude</u> and <u>direction</u> of the different forces exerted on an object by looking <u>only</u> at its motion, without reference to the objects exerting the forces? Explain.

R4. A thrown ball is observed to be moving at a nearly constant speed prior to hitting the ground. Use Newton's second law and your knowledge about forces to deduce as much as you can about this situation.

More Analyzing Physical Situations Using Newton's First and Second Laws

Purpose and Expected Outcome

This activity is a continuation of the previous one. Before, we used strobe diagrams to represent the motion of different objects. Now, we will use plots of position vs. time and velocity vs. time, as well as equations. You will learn how to analyze the motion of objects and learn how to describe some of the forces acting on these objects.

Prior Experience / Knowledge Needed

You should understand plots of position, velocity, and acceleration vs. time. You should know how to determine two of them if given the third. You should be familiar with vectors and be able to find components of vectors. You should be familiar with mathematical expressions of position and velocity as functions of time. You should have been introduced to Newton's laws of Motion, especially the first and second laws.

Explanation of Activity

This activity consists of 3 situations. For each situation, the motion of an object will be given using either kinematic plots or kinematic equations or a combination of both. Answer each of the questions posed about the situation using Newton's laws as much as possible.

SITUATION A: Motion of a Marble Rolling Up an Incline

A marble rolls up an incline, stops near the top, and rolls back down. During this time period, the position of the marble along the incline is given by:

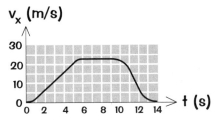

$$x = (120 \text{cm/s})t - (90 \text{cm/s}^2)t^2$$

Use this equation to help you answer the questions below.

A1. What is the x-component of the acceleration of the marble as a function of time?

A2. (a) What is the y-component of the position of the marble as a function of time?
   (b) Use this to find the y-component of the acceleration as a function of time.

A3. What is the direction of the acceleration of the marble as it rolls up the incline?

A4. What is the direction of the marble's acceleration when it is at rest near the top of the incline?

A5. What is the direction of the marble's acceleration as it rolls back down the incline?

A6. Is there ever a time when the net force on the marble is zero?

A7. Is your answer to question A6 consistent with your answers to questions A3–A5? Explain using Newton's laws.

SITUATION B: Motion of a Car Driving Along the Road

A car drives down a long, straight road according to the velocity graph shown to the right. Use this graph to help you answer the questions below.

B1. When is there a net force exerted on the car? Explain.

B2. When is the net force exerted on the car the largest? Explain.

Activity 56
More Analyzing Physical Situations Using Newton's First and Second Laws

B3. When is the net force on the car changing? Explain.

B4. For the time period between $t = 6$s and $t = 9$s, list the forces exerted on the car, indicate the agent exerting each force, and draw a free-body diagram for the car.

B5. Describe a scenario for the car that would correspond to the velocity graph given above. (That is, create a story to go with the given motion of the car.)

SITUATION C: Motion of a Student Walking to School

A student walks to school one morning according to the plots of position vs. time shown below. Assume that the student walks at constant speed during the whole trip. Ignore air resistance.

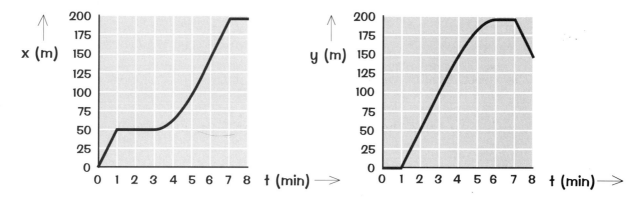

Use these graphs to help you answer the questions below.

C1. On an xy grid, make a strobe diagram for the motion of the student at one-minute intervals.

C2. Where is the school located relative to the student's starting point?

C3. At what times is the velocity of the student changing? Explain.

C4. At what times is there a net force on the student? Explain.

C5. At those times when there is a net force on the student, what agent provides the unbalanced force to cause the observed motion? Explain.

Reflection and Integration

R1. The *x*-coordinate of an object as a function of time is shown to the right. What can you say about the forces exerted on the object during this time period?

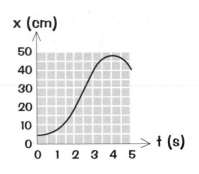

R2. For one of the situations (A, B, or C), there is a net force exerted even though the object is at rest. Which one? When does this occur? Explain, using Newton's laws.

R3. For <u>at least</u> one of the situations, there is a net force exerted even though the speed is not changing. Which one(s)? For each, when does this occur? Explain, again using Newton's laws.

R4. For <u>two</u> of the situations, the net force is directly opposite the direction of motion. Which two? When does this occur? Explain.

R5. For one of the situations, the net force is neither in the direction of motion nor opposite the direction of motion, but some direction in between. Which one? When does this occur? Explain.

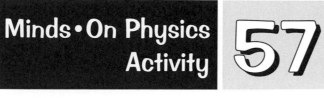
Relating the Forces Exerted on an Object to its Motion

Purpose and Expected Outcome

After completing this activity, you will be able to generalize the central features of Newton's laws and how they relate to the motion of objects.

Prior Experience / Knowledge Needed

You should be familiar with different ways of representing the motion of objects. You should understand the relationship between kinematic quantities, like position, velocity, and acceleration. You should be familiar with free-body diagrams, common forces, their agents, and Newton's laws.

Explanation of Activity and Example

In this activity, you are given a set of conditions or constraints, and you must describe a situation that fits <u>all</u> of the given constraints.

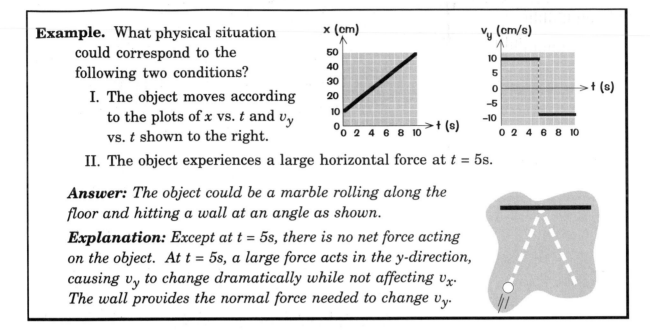

Example. What physical situation could correspond to the following two conditions?

   I. The object moves according to the plots of x vs. t and v_y vs. t shown to the right.

   II. The object experiences a large horizontal force at $t = 5$s.

Answer: The object could be a marble rolling along the floor and hitting a wall at an angle as shown.

Explanation: Except at $t = 5$s, there is no net force acting on the object. At $t = 5$s, a large force acts in the y-direction, causing v_y to change dramatically while not affecting v_x. The wall provides the normal force needed to change v_y.

A1.   What situation could correspond to the following conditions?

   I. There are <u>no</u> unbalanced forces exerted on the object; — and —

   II. The direction of motion is perpendicular to <u>all</u> forces exerted on the object.

A2.   What situation could correspond to these conditions?

   I. The net force is perpendicular to the direction of motion; — and —

   II. The speed of the object is constant.

A3.   What situation could fit the following constraints?

   I. The object is at rest; — and —

   II. There are three forces exerted on the object; — and —

   III. All three forces have the <u>same</u> magnitude.

continued

A4. What situation could fit <u>all</u> of the following constraints?

    I. There are exactly 3 forces exerted on the object:

        – force A points opposite to the direction of motion;
        – force B points straight downward at all times;
        – force C points perpendicular to the direction of motion.

    II. Force A is exerted <u>only</u> when the object is moving.

    III. At <u>exactly</u> one instant, the free-body diagram looks like this:

    IV. Initially, the object is at rest (so force A is not exerted).

C ↑

A ←

B ↓

Reflection

R1. Can an object have an acceleration even though there are no forces exerted on it? Explain. If it is possible, give an example of a situation in which this is true.

R2. Does the direction of motion help you to find the direction of the net force? Explain.

R3. (a) What feature of a velocity vs. time graph tells you about the relative size of the net force exerted on an object?

    (b) What feature tells you about the direction of the net force?

R4. How would you find the net force exerted on an object if you were given the kinematic equations for its position? For instance, if $x(t) = 3\text{m} - 4\text{m/s}\, t + 1\text{m/s}^2\, t^2$, how would you find the net force?

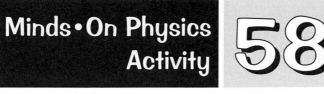

Making Distinctions Between Newton's Second and Third Laws

Purpose and Expected Outcome

In this activity, we will concentrate on Newton's third law of Motion. After finishing this activity you should understand better how to apply Newton's third law and how to distinguish it from the second law.

Prior Experience / Knowledge Needed

You should be familiar with the common forces and interactions between objects. You should understand free-body diagrams and vectors. You should know Newton's second law of Motion.

NEWTON'S THIRD LAW OF MOTION

Whenever two objects interact with one another, each object exerts a force on the other. These two forces are always equal to each other in magnitude, and opposite to each other in direction. All known forces obey this law.

Sometimes Newton's third law is stated this way:

"For each action, there is an equal and opposite reaction,"

and the pair of forces is often referred to as an "action–reaction" pair. Unfortunately, this wording suggests that one of the forces acts first, then the other acts in reaction to the first. This implication is misleading, because in fact both forces act at the exact same time. When I push on a wall, I feel the wall "pushing back". I cannot push on the wall without the wall pushing back.

continued

Imagine that you are holding a rock in your hand. The earth pulls the rock downward, and if you let go, the forces become "unbalanced" and the rock accelerates toward the earth. That's Newton's <u>first</u> law. To keep the rock at rest, you must "balance" the gravitational force by applying a normal force upward. The rock's acceleration is zero, so the net force must also be zero. That's Newton's <u>second</u> law. Finally, the rock is pushing downward on your hand with a normal force equal in magnitude and opposite in direction to the normal force you are applying to it. That's Newton's <u>third</u> law.

The following table summarizes the differences between "action–reaction" forces and "balancing" forces, and will help you to understand Newton's laws:

Action–reaction forces...	**while balancing forces...**
1. *<u>always</u> come in pairs,*	*only sometimes come in pairs.*
2. *are <u>always</u> equal and opposite,*	*are only <u>sometimes</u> equal and opposite.*
3. *<u>always</u> exist, as long as there are two objects interacting,*	*are appropriate <u>only</u> when the net force on an object is zero.*
4. *<u>always</u> act on different objects,*	*<u>always</u> act on the same object.*
5. *are <u>always</u> the same type (normal, friction, tension, etc.),*	*are usually different types.*
6. *are used in connection with Newton's <u>third</u> law,*	*are used in connection with Newton's <u>second</u> law.*

Many reaction forces (like the gravitational forces that objects exert on the earth) are ignored because their effects are negligible. Newton's third law is a useful problem-solving tool and has important consequences for the observed motion of large-scale objects. Understanding this law will be critical to understanding momentum and momentum conservation.

Explanation of Activity and Example

PART A: Identifying Action–Reaction Pairs of Forces

For each of the situations below, (a) list all the action–reaction pairs of forces exerted on the objects, and (b) indicate which pair of objects is interacting to produce each pair of forces. (There should be <u>no</u> unpaired forces!) (c) If requested, draw and label a free-body diagram for each object.

continued

Example. A soccer player kicks a ball.

Answer: *There are three objects to consider: (1) the player, (2) the ball, and (3) the earth.*

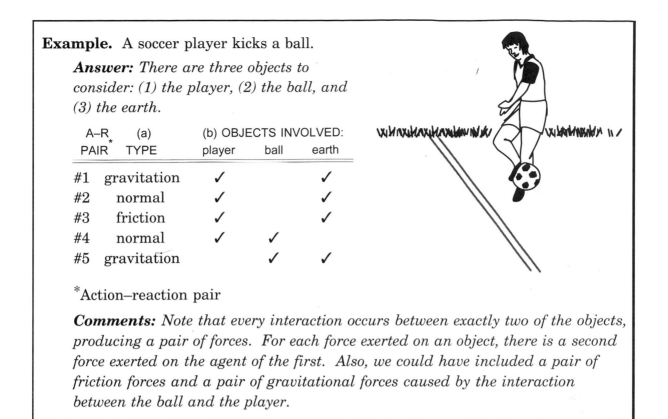

A–R PAIR*	(a) TYPE	(b) OBJECTS INVOLVED: player	ball	earth
#1	gravitation	✓		✓
#2	normal	✓		✓
#3	friction	✓		✓
#4	normal	✓	✓	
#5	gravitation		✓	✓

*Action–reaction pair

Comments: *Note that every interaction occurs between exactly two of the objects, producing a pair of forces. For each force exerted on an object, there is a second force exerted on the agent of the first. Also, we could have included a pair of friction forces and a pair of gravitational forces caused by the interaction between the ball and the player.*

A1. A bowling ball strikes the head pin. Consider only the ball, the head pin, and the earth.

A2. A skydiver falls to earth at constant velocity just before hitting the ground. Consider only the skydiver, the parachute (<u>including</u> the strings), and the earth.

(a) For each interaction, identify the type of force exerted.

(b) Identify the objects interacting to produce each pair of forces.

(c) For each object, draw and label a free-body diagram showing all the forces exerted on it.

continued

A3. A coffee mug and a large dictionary are stacked on top of a table as shown. (Skip parts (a) and (b), unless it helps you to answer (c).)

   (a) For each interaction, identify the type of force exerted.

   (b) Identify the objects interacting to produce each pair of forces.

   (c) For each object (the dictionary, the mug, the table, and the earth) draw and label a free-body diagram showing all the forces acting on it.

   (d) For each of the forces on the coffee mug, indicate its "reaction" force.

PART B: Reasoning Using Newton's Laws

In each of the situations presented below, Newton's laws are used to provide an explanation, to predict an outcome, or to determine the forces acting on an object. For each situation, you should (a) determine if you agree or disagree with the statements made about the situation, then (b) explain why you agree or disagree.

B1. A horse pulls on a wagon as shown below. Newton's third law states that the force exerted on the horse by the wagon must be equal and opposite to the force exerted on the wagon by the horse. Therefore, no matter how hard the horse pulls on the wagon, the wagon pulls back just as hard, making it impossible for the horse to move the wagon.

   (a) Do you agree or disagree with these statements?

   (b) Explain.

continued

B2. A girl throws a rubber ball against the side of a building as shown. While in contact with the building, the <u>only</u> forces acting on the ball are a normal force due to the building and possibly a friction force. Since the building does not move, the ball exerts <u>no</u> force on the building when it bounces off.

(a) Do you agree or disagree with these statements?

(b) Explain.

B3.

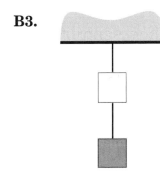

Two blocks are attached to two massless strings as shown to the left. Both blocks are at rest. The free-body diagram for the <u>upper</u> block is shown to the right. The three forces on the upper block are:

1. the gravitational force exerted by the earth on the <u>upper</u> block;

2. the tension force exerted by the <u>top</u> string; — and —

3. the gravitational force exerted by the earth on the <u>bottom</u> block.

(a) Do you agree or disagree with these statements?

(b) Explain.

B4. A father is rollerblading with his daughter. The father gives the daughter a huge push, causing each of them to move in opposite directions away from their original position. However, the daughter travels faster and farther than the father does in the same amount of time. Therefore, we know the net force on her must have been greater than the net force on the father. This is reasonable since it was the father who did the pushing. If their positions were reversed and she pushed him instead, he would travel faster and farther than she would.

(a) Do you agree or disagree with these statements?

(b) Explain.

Integration of Ideas

A book slides across the floor, slowing down to a stop in 3 meters. Consider the floor to be part of the earth.

I1. What forces act on the book as it slides across the floor? What agent exerts each of these forces?

I2. Draw and label a free-body diagram for the book.

I3. Draw and label a free-body diagram for the earth showing the interactions between the earth and the book. Which law(s) did you use to do this?

I4. According to your free-body diagram, are there any unbalanced forces on the earth? If so, what must be true about the motion of the earth? Which law(s) did you use to determine this?

I5. Does this result make sense to you? Explain, and resolve any inconsistencies between what Newton's laws predict and what you would expect.

Reflection

R1. A normal force is exerted on a particular object. What can you say about its reaction force?

R2. Two blocks are at rest as shown. Also shown are their free-body diagrams.

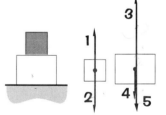

   (a) Of the five forces labeled in the free-body diagram, which two form an action–reaction pair? Explain.

   (b) Which block is heavier? Explain.

R3. (a) In many of the situations presented in this activity, there were two or more objects interacting with the earth (and each other). Is there a gravitational force between these objects? For instance, is there a gravitational force between the two blocks in the situation above? Explain.

   (b) If so, why do we neglect the gravitational force in these situations?

R4. (a) Do the moon and the sun exert gravitational forces on objects near the earth? Explain.

   (b) If so, why do we neglect the effect of the sun and moon and other celestial objects?

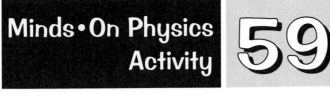

Reasoning with Newton's Laws

Purpose and Expected Outcome

In this activity, you will deepen your understanding of Newton's laws and how they relate to physical situations.

Prior Experience / Knowledge Needed

You should be familiar with Newton's laws of motion. Also, you should be able to draw and label free-body diagrams, and you should be able to determine the components of vectors.

Explanation of Activity and Example

In this activity, you are given a variety of physical situations, and you are asked to make comparisons of different physical quantities such as acceleration and force. Answer each question and explain the reasoning you used. The main emphasis is on the explanation, rather than the comparison. You might guess the right answer, but the explanation will show whether or not you have understood the situation.

Example. Two blocks are pulled to the left at constant speed as shown. The mass of each block is proportional to its size. All coefficients of friction are the same. Both cases are the same except that the blocks are reversed in case II. In which case is the normal force on the lefthand block larger? Explain.

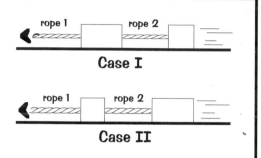

Answer: *Case I. The blocks are not accelerating, so by Newton's 2nd law, the net force on each block must be zero. Therefore, the tension force due to rope 1 balances the tension force due to rope 2 and the force of friction, and the normal force balances the weight of the block. Because the lefthand block in case I has the larger weight, case I has the larger normal force.*

SITUATION A

Two blocks are pulled to the left at constant speed as shown in the example above. The mass of each block is proportional to its size. All coefficients of friction are the same. Both cases are the same except that the positions of the blocks are reversed in case II.

A1. In which case is the tension in rope 1 larger? Explain.

A2. In which case is the tension in rope 2 larger? Explain.

Suppose now that the speed of the blocks in case I is twice the speed of the blocks in case II. (That is, $v_I = 2v_{II}$.)

A3. In which case is the tension in rope 1 larger? Explain.

A4. In which case is the <u>difference</u> between the tensions in the ropes larger? Explain.

SITUATION B

Consider the two cases shown to the right. The blocks are identical, both surfaces are frictionless, and the tensions in the two ropes are the same.

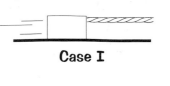

Case I

B1. In which case does the block have the larger acceleration? Explain.

Case II

B2. In which case does the surface exert the larger normal force? Explain.

Now assume that there is friction between the block and the surface in each case. Assume also that the coefficients of friction are the same and that the blocks are each being pulled at constant speed.

B3. Are the tension forces in the two cases still equal to each other? Explain.

B4. In which case is the tension in the rope larger? Explain.

SITUATION C

Two cars, Y and Z, are traveling side-by-side down a long, straight highway. The net force acting on each car as a function of time is shown to the right. The cars are identical. At $t = 0$, both cars are at rest, and they are located next to each other, as shown below.

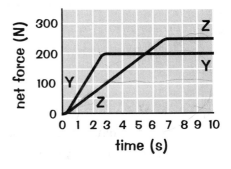

C1. Is there ever a time when the two cars have the same acceleration? If so, when does this occur? Explain.

C2. Which car has the larger velocity at $t = 4s$? Explain.

Now assume that car Y has twice the mass of car Z. That is, $m_Y = 2m_Z$.

C3. Is there ever a time when the two cars have the same acceleration? If so, when does this occur? Explain.

C4. Which car has the larger velocity at $t = 10s$? Explain.

SITUATION D

A spring is compressed between two blocks as shown. The surface is horizontal and frictionless. The blocks are released from rest at the same instant.

D1. Which block has the larger net force exerted on it just after they are released? Explain.

D2. Which block has the larger acceleration just after they are released? Explain.

SITUATION E

A block is suspended inside a wooden crate, which is placed on a child's wagon as shown. Someone pulls on the wagon, causing the whole system to accelerate to the right.

E1. Which string exerts the larger tension force on the block? Explain.

E2. Now someone pulls just hard enough to keep the system moving at constant speed. Which string applies the larger tension force in this case? Explain.

Reflection

R1. In how many of the situations did you use a free-body diagram to help you answer the questions? In what ways did they help you? In those cases that you did not use a free-body diagram, did you struggle with the questions? Comment on the usefulness of free-body diagrams.

R2. Consider each of the situations in this activity. What was helpful for answering the questions? For instance, which of Newton's laws did you use (if any)? What techniques did you use (such as finding the slope of a graph or drawing a free-body diagram)? What ideas did you need to understand (such as position or velocity)? Examine each situation separately, and list what you used to answer the questions.

R3. Combine all the items listed in R2 into a single list showing the relative importance of each. Start with the most important and end with the least.

More Reasoning
with Newton's Laws

Purpose and Expected Outcome

In this activity, you will again use Newton's laws to analyze the motion of objects, except that now the situations are increasingly complex. You will see, however, that even though the situation may be complicated, we can always break down the situation into much simpler parts by isolating individual objects and analyzing the motion of each using Newton's laws.

Prior Experience / Knowledge Needed

You should be able to draw and label free-body diagrams, and you should be familiar with all the common forces. You should know how to apply each of Newton's Three laws of Motion, especially Newton's second and third laws. You should have some experience analyzing physical situations.

Explanation of Activity

There are three parts to this activity. In each part, you will be given a set of three physical situations to analyze and compare. For each set, you will be asked to answer specific questions about the different situations. As you think about these questions, consider the forces on individual objects, and consider how Newton's second and third laws apply.

PART A: Analyzing Different Modes of Transportation

Consider the following three situations:

SITUATION I: A magnet (A) attracts a metal bar (B) attached to a wagon (C).

SITUATION II: A carrot attracts a horse attached to a wagon.

SITUATION III: A person rides a unicycle.

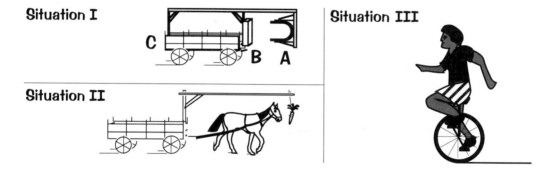

A1. In which of the situations (if any) will the system move? Explain.

A2. In those situations in which the system moves, what force causes the motion? Explain.

A3. In each situation, what is the reaction force corresponding to the force causing motion? On what object is the reaction force exerted?

PART B: Analyzing a System of Three Blocks on a Horizontal Surface

Consider the following three situations:

SITUATION I: Three blocks are sitting on a smooth horizontal surface as shown, with block C in contact with a brick wall. A horizontal force is applied to block A.

SITUATION II: This is the same as situation I, except that there is no wall to prevent the blocks from moving. The surface is frictionless.

SITUATION III: This is the same as situation II, except that now there is sufficient friction between the blocks and the surface to prevent motion. If block C were removed, blocks A and B would remain at rest.

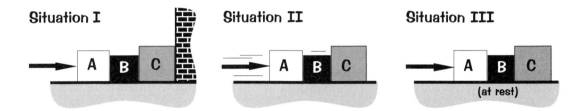

Note: In all three situations the magnitude of the applied force is the same.

B1. In which of the situations are the blocks accelerating? Explain.

B2. In which of the situations is the net force on block C the largest? Explain.

B3. In which of the situations is the force on block B due to block C the largest? Explain.

B4. Which of your answers depend upon the masses of the blocks? Explain.

PART C: Analyzing a System of Blocks and Strings

Consider the following three situations:

SITUATION I: Two identical blocks are hanging, one from each end of a massless string. The string passes over frictionless, massless pulleys.

SITUATION II: A single block is hanging from one end of a massless string, which passes over a frictionless, massless pulley and is attached to a brick wall.

SITUATION III: This is the same as situation I, except that now the string is broken into two pieces, and a third block is connected to both free ends. The surface is frictionless.

Situation I   Situation II   Situation III

Note: Because the strings and the pulleys are massless and the pulleys are frictionless, you may assume that the tension is the same everywhere in any one piece of string. Initially all systems are at rest.

C1. In which of the situations (if any) will the system move when released from rest? Explain.

C2. In which of the situations is the tension in the string the largest? Explain.

C3. Suppose that there is friction between block C and the table. How would your answers change? Explain.

Integration of Ideas

Consider the following three situations. In each case, a block is hanging from a massless string, which is connected to a second block. The second block is connected to a second string which is attached to a wall. Blocks A and B each weigh 5N, and block C weighs 40N. The surface is frictionless. In situations II and III, string 2 is suddenly cut, allowing the system to accelerate.

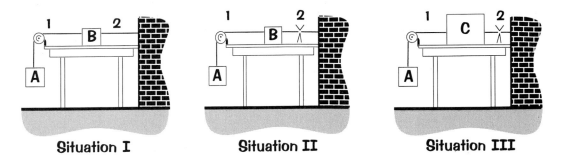

Situation I   Situation II   Situation III

Note: Each of these questions requires only a short answer. Be prepared to explain how you answered each question.

I1. What is the tension in string 1 of situation I?

I2. Consider block A in situation II. There are two forces exerted on A: (1) a gravitational force is exerted downward, and (2) a tension force is exerted upward.
   (a) What is the direction of the acceleration of block A?
   (b) Is there a net force on A?
   (c) What is the direction of the net force?
   (d) Which is larger, the gravitational force or the tension force?
   (e) Is the tension in string 1 larger or smaller than in Situation I?

I3. Consider block A in situation III.
   (a) Is its acceleration larger or smaller than in situation II?
   (b) Is the net force on A larger or smaller than in situation II?
   (c) Is the tension in string 1 larger or smaller than in situation II?

Reflection

R1. Two objects are interacting near the surface of the earth. The net force on one is twice the net force on the other. What can you say about ...

(a) ... their positions?

(b) ... their velocities?

(c) ... their accelerations?

(d) ... the force that each exerts on the other?

(e) ... the force that each each exerts on the earth?

R2. You are driving in a car. For each of the following quantities, compare its value for you to its value for the car at any arbitrary instant of time.

(a) mass

(b) position

(c) velocity

(d) speed

(e) acceleration

(f) net force

(g) normal force due to each other

(h) gravitational force

Using Newton's Laws to Determine the Magnitudes and Directions of Forces

Purpose and Expected Outcome

In this activity, you will learn how to properly apply the three basic ways to find the magnitude and direction of any particular force:

(1) using an empirical law (such as $F_g = mg$ or $\mathbf{F}_s = -k\mathbf{x}$);

(2) using Newton's second law ($\mathbf{F}_{net} = m\mathbf{a}$); or

(3) using Newton's third law ($\mathbf{F}_{\text{on 1, due to 2}} = -\mathbf{F}_{\text{on 2, due to 1}}$).

Prior Experience / Knowledge Needed

You should be able to draw and label free-body diagrams, and you should be familiar with all the common forces. You should know which forces can be calculated using empirical laws (assuming certain information is given) and which forces can <u>never</u> be found using an empirical law. You should know Newton's second and third laws, and you should know how they apply in common situations. Finally, you should be able to find the acceleration of an object given other kinematic information (such as positions at different times, or plots of velocity vs. time, or mathematical expressions for position or velocity as functions of time).

Explanation of Activity and Example

This activity consists of two parts. In the first part, a number of physical situations will be described and free-body diagrams will be provided for each object in each situation. You will indicate how you will determine the value of each force. Then, in the second part, you will draw your own free-body diagrams and calculate the values of as many forces as possible. Use a value of $g = 10\text{N/kg}$ throughout.

PART A: Indicating <u>How</u> You Will Determine the Value of a Force

For the forces shown in the free-body diagrams, (a) list the forces in the <u>order</u> in which you will calculate them; and (b) indicate <u>how</u> you will determine the value of each one. Your choices are:

(G)   its value has already been given;

(EFL) using an empirical force law;

(N2L) using Newton's second law; and

(N3L) using Newton's third law.

Then, (c) explain how you would calculate the value of each force in the order specified. (Some hints are provided.) Finally, in (d), explain how you would calculate certain physical quantities using the values of the forces.

E1. Two books are stacked on top of one another as shown. The upper book (#1) has a mass of 3kg, and the lower book (#2) has a mass of 2kg. Both books are at rest.

Answer:

	(a)	(b)	(c)

Order	Force	Method	Explanation
1	F_{g1}	EFL	$F_{g1} = m_1 g$. Both m_1 and g are known.
2	F_{g2}	EFL	$F_{g2} = m_2 g$. Both m_2 and g are known.
3	F_{N12}	N2L	Book 1 is at rest, so its acceleration is zero, which implies that the net force acting on it is zero. Therefore, $F_{N12} = F_{g1}$. F_{g1} is known from step 1.
4	F_{N21}	N3L	F_{N21} is the reaction force to F_{N12}. Therefore, they both have the <u>same</u> magnitude: $F_{N21} = F_{N12}$. F_{N12} is known from step 3.
5	F_N	N2L	Book 2 is at rest, so its acceleration is zero, which implies that the net force acting on it is zero. Therefore, $F_N = F_{g2} + F_{N21}$. F_{g2} is known from step 2, and F_{N21} is known from step 4.

continued

A1. A block hangs at rest from a spring having spring constant 10N/cm. The spring is stretched 2.5cm from its relaxed state.

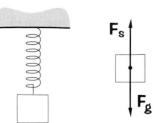

(a) List the forces on the block in the order you would calculate them.

(b) Indicate how you will determine the value of each force.

(c) Explain how you will determine the value of each force.

(d) How would you find the mass of the block?

A2. A 10kg box is pulled along a horizontal surface by means of a rope held at an angle of 40° above the horizontal as shown. The tension in the rope is 60N and the friction force on the box is 32N.

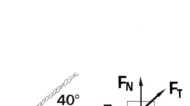

(a) List the forces on the box in the order you would calculate them.

(b) Indicate how you will determine the value of each force.

(c) Explain how you will determine the value of each force.

(d) How would you find the coefficient of kinetic friction between the box and the plane?

A3. An 8kg sled slides down a hill having coefficient of sliding friction equal to 0.3 and coefficient of static friction equal to 0.4.

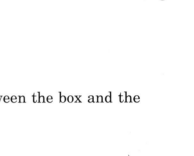

(a) List the forces on the sled in the order you would calculate them.

(b) Indicate how you will determine the value of each force. (**Hint:** F_N is found using N2L.)

(c) Explain how you will determine the value of each force. (**Hint:** There is no motion perpendicular to the incline. If we choose the y-axis to be perpendicular to the incline, then the y-component of the acceleration is zero, and the y-component of the net force is also zero. So, the magnitude of the normal force must be equal to the y-component of the gravitational force. Therefore, $F_N = F_g \cos \theta$. F_g is known from step 1, and θ is the given angle that the hill makes with the horizontal.)

(d) How would you find the acceleration of the sled?

continued

A4. A book slides across the gymnasium floor having coefficient of kinetic friction equal to 0.5. The force of friction on the book is 2.4N.

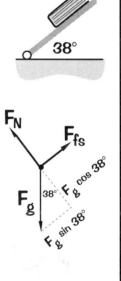

(a) List the forces on the book in the order you would calculate them.

(b) Indicate how you will determine the value of each force.

(c) Explain how you will determine the value of each force.

(d) How would you find the mass of the book?

PART B: Calculating the Values of Forces

For each problem situation, (a) draw and label a free-body diagram for each object in the situation; (b) determine the values of as many forces as possible; and (c) answer the question posed. Use $g = 10$N/kg throughout.

E2. A book weighing 5N is placed on an adjustable incline as shown. The incline is slowly raised until the book just starts to slide. This occurs at an angle of 38°. What is the coefficient of static friction?

Answer: *The free-body diagram for the book is shown to the right. We use Newton's second law to find F_N and F_{fs}. The book is at rest, so the net force is zero. Therefore the normal force is equal to the component of the gravitational force perpendicular to the incline, and the static friction force is equal to the component of the gravitational force parallel to the incline:*

$$F_g = 5\text{N} \qquad \text{(given)}$$
$$F_N = F_g \cos 38° = (5\text{N})(0.788) = 3.94\text{N} \qquad \text{(by N2L)}$$
$$F_{fs} = F_g \sin 38° = (5\text{N})(0.616) = 3.08\text{N} \qquad \text{(by N2L)}$$

We use an empirical force law to find μ_s. The coefficient of static friction is the ratio of the __maximum__ static friction force and the normal force. Since 38° is the largest angle, 3.08N is the maximum F_{fs}. So, $\mu_s = F_{fs,max} \div F_N = 3.08\text{N} \div 3.94\text{N} = 0.78$.

Note: *We could have found μ_s without knowing the weight of the book, since $F_{fs,max} \div F_N = F_g \sin 38° \div F_g \cos 38° = \tan 38° = 0.78$.*

continued

B1. A block hangs at rest from a spring having spring constant 10N/cm. The spring is stretched 2.5cm from its relaxed state. What is the mass of the block?

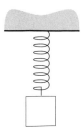

B2. You are on a roller coaster, and the ride is about to finish. As your car approaches the unloading point, the acceleration is very large, so you use your arms to push on the front of the car and keep yourself from sliding in your seat. Assuming the roller coaster slows down from 40mi/h (about 18m/s) to a stop in 2s, how hard do you push horizontally during this 2s period? (Neglect frictional effects.)

B3. Using the information from the previous problem, assume the car weighs 10,000N, and that 8 people are all pushing on the car. Estimate the force of friction on the car.

B4. You are driving down a straight horizontal road at 35mi/h (about 15.6m/s). Suddenly a ball bounces in front of your car, so you slam on the brakes and slide for about 30m before stopping. What is the coefficient of sliding friction between the tires and the road?

Reflection

R1. You would like to find the weight of an object. One way to determine its weight is to measure its mass and multiply by g. Is this the only way of finding its weight? Explain. What principle are you using to find its weight?

R2. List those types of forces whose values may be determined using an empirical force law. For each type of force, what information is needed to determine its value?

R3. List those types of forces whose values may be determined using Newton's second or third law. For each type of force, what information is needed to determine its value?

R4. Consider problem B3 (finding the friction force on the roller coaster car). Typical values of the coefficient of sliding friction are at most 0.4, yet the force of friction is larger than the weight of the car. How is this possible? Suggest a design that might produce this result.

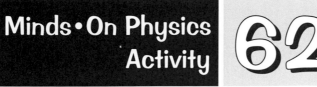
Solving Problems
with Newton's Laws

Purpose and Expected Outcome

In this activity, you will use Newton's laws to analyze the physical situations and focus your attention on the forces that are exerted on individual objects. After completing this activity, you will see that solving *dynamics* problems usually involves relating the net force on an object to its acceleration. The acceleration can then be used to predict the position and velocity of the object at different times. You will also learn the roles of empirical laws and Newton's third law in helping you solve problems.

Prior Experience / Knowledge Needed

DYNAMICS

You now have all the skills needed to solve problems: You are familiar with Newton's laws and how they apply to physical situations. You know the empirical laws and when each can be used to determine the value of a force. You can draw free-body diagrams and use them to analyze physical situations. You know the relationships between position, velocity, and acceleration, and you can represent each as a function of time using either a graph or a mathematical expression. You understand vectors and you know how to find the component of a vector. This is *dynamics*, the study of the relationship between the forces exerted on objects and the kinematic response of those objects.

continued

There are two distinct ways to think about dynamics problems, each of which has Newton's second law at its core. For many problems, we use empirical laws or other given information to estimate or calculate the net force exerted on an object. Then we use $\mathbf{F}_{net} = m\mathbf{a}$ to find its acceleration, and kinematics to predict its change in position and velocity. For others, we do the opposite. We observe the change in position and/or velocity of an object, and estimate or calculate its acceleration. Then we (again) use $\mathbf{F}_{net} = m\mathbf{a}$, except now it is used to learn something about the forces exerted on the object. As you work through these problems, keep in mind these two ways of thinking about dynamics problems.

Explanation of Activity

In this activity, you will explore many different ways of using given information to solve problems with Newton's laws.

A1. A bowling ball hits a pin head on, knocking it forward. The ball has a mass $M_{ball} = 6.8$kg, and the pin has a mass $M_{pin} = 2$kg. The total interaction time is 0.01 seconds, during which the average force on the pin is 1500N. The pin is initially at rest.

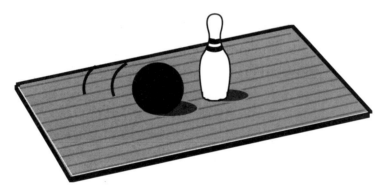

(a) What is the average acceleration of the pin while in contact with the ball?

(b) What is the final velocity of the pin?

(c) Is it possible to find the final velocity of the ball? Why or why not? Explain.

(d) Can we find the change in the ball's velocity? Explain. If so, what is it?

continued

A2. A father and daughter are roller blading. Initially both are standing still in the middle of a large flat horizontal area as shown below. At $t = 0$s, the daughter pushes her father according to the plot to the right. The father's mass is 80kg, and the daughter's mass is 60kg.

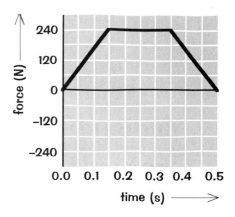

(a) Sketch the force on the daughter as a function of time. Explain how you determined this graph.

(b) Sketch the accelerations of the father and the daughter as functions of time. Be sure to label your vertical axis and to indicate which graph corresponds to the father and which corresponds to the daughter.

(c) Assume that there are no frictional effects on either the father or the daughter. What is the final velocity of the father? What is the final velocity of the daughter? Explain.

(d) Multiply the mass of each person by his/her velocity. How do these values compare to each other?

A3. Two ropes are used to pull two blocks as shown. The velocity of block A is found at 1s intervals and has been plotted as shown. The weight of block B is 10N and the tension in rope 2 is 2.5N as observed by a spring scale.

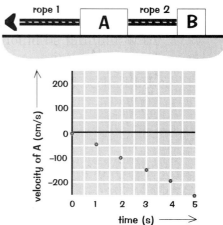

(a) Estimate the acceleration of block A. Explain how you calculated this value.

(b) Estimate the acceleration of block B. How did you determine this value?

(c) Other than a gravitational force, a tension force, and a normal force, what force <u>must</u> be exerted on block B? Explain. What is the magnitude and direction of this force? What other quantity may be calculated from this value?

(d) Is there enough information to find the tension force on A due to rope 1? If so, calculate its value. If not, what additional information is needed to find it?

continued

A4. Two blocks are attached to a pulley as shown to the right. The larger block has a mass of 3kg and is observed to fall 1 meter in 1 second starting from rest. You may ignore the mass of the pulley. You should assume the tension in the string is the same throughout its length.

(a) What is the acceleration of the 3kg block?

(b) What is the tension force exerted on the 3kg block?

(c) What is the tension force exerted on the other block? Explain.

(d) What is the acceleration of the smaller block? Explain.

(e) What is the mass of the smaller block? Explain.

Reflection

R1. Consider each of the problems in this activity. Make a table by indicating how you determined the acceleration and the net force of each object.

	How did you determine ...		
Object	(a) ... a_x?	(b) ... a_y?	(c) ... $\mathbf{F}_{net}$?
A1. bowling pin			
bowling ball			
A2. father on roller blades			
daughter on roller blades			
A3. block A			
block B			
A4. large block			
small block			

R2. How many different methods do you know for finding the acceleration of an object? Describe the methods as generally as possible. (Try not to be too specific. Rather, try to divide the different methods into a small number of major categories, and then describe the categories.)

R3. How many different methods do you know for finding the net force on an object? Describe the methods as generally as possible.

Analyzing Forces
without Empirical Laws

Purpose and Expected Outcome

In this activity, you will learn more about using Newton's second law (rather than empirical laws) to determine the values of different forces.

Prior Experience / Knowledge Needed

You should be able to draw and label free-body diagrams, and you should be familiar with the normal force, the tension force and the force of static friction. You should also know Newton's second law. You should be able to find the components of vectors. You should also be familiar with the 3-4-5 triangle (a right triangle, the ratio of whose sides is $3 : 4 : 5$.)

Explanation of Activity and Example

A small wooden crate weighing 100N is pulled (but <u>not</u> moved) by tension in a rope as shown. The crate is at rest, so the vector sum of all the forces exerted on it must be zero. We consider four different angles for the rope (labeled A1, A2, A3 and A4). For each angle, we consider three different physical situations (labeled a, b, and c).

In each case, two of the four forces on the crate are given. Determine the values of the other two forces.

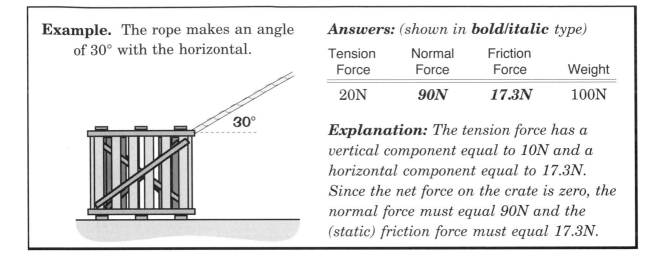

Example. The rope makes an angle of 30° with the horizontal.

*Answers: (shown in **bold/italic** type)*

Tension Force	Normal Force	Friction Force	Weight
20N	***90N***	***17.3N***	100N

Explanation: *The tension force has a vertical component equal to 10N and a horizontal component equal to 17.3N. Since the net force on the crate is zero, the normal force must equal 90N and the (static) friction force must equal 17.3N.*

A1. The rope is horizontal.

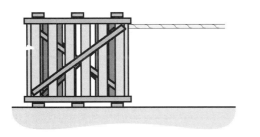

	Tension Force	Normal Force	Friction Force	Weight
(a)	20N			100N
(b)			10N	100N
(c)	0N			100N

continued

A2. The rope makes an angle of 37° with the horizontal.

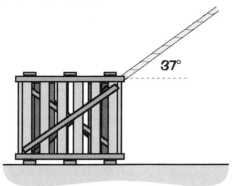

	Tension Force	Normal Force	Friction Force	Weight
(a)	20N			100N
(b)		76N		100N
(c)			12N	100N

A3. The rope makes an angle of 53° with the horizontal.

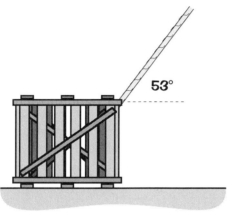

	Tension Force	Normal Force	Friction Force	Weight
(a)	20N			100N
(b)		76N		100N
(c)			24N	100N

A4. The rope is vertical.

	Tension Force	Normal Force	Friction Force	Weight
(a)	20N			100N
(b)		0N		100N
(c)	0N			100N

Integration of Ideas

For each question below, consider the same system of a wooden crate at rest on a horizontal surface with a rope attached, but consider all angles from 0° to 360°.

Note: Angles are measured counterclockwise from the horizontal. That is, 0° is to the right, 90° is up, 180° is to the left, and 270° is down.

I1. Keeping the tension and the weight constant, for which angle(s)...

(a) ... is the static friction force a maximum? a minimum? Explain.

(b) ... is the normal force a maximum? a minimum? Explain.

I2. When the rope is horizontal, what is the relationship between...

(a) ... the tension force and the static friction force? Explain.

(b) ... the normal force and the weight? Explain.

I3. When the rope is between 0° and 90°, which is larger (or are they the same)...

(a) ... the tension force or the static friction force? Explain.

(b) ... the normal force or the weight? Explain.

I4. By changing <u>only</u> the angle of the rope, is it possible to make...

(a) ... the normal force greater than the weight? Explain.

(b) ... the tension force smaller than the static friction force? Explain.

Reflection

R1. Reconsider situation A1, part (a).

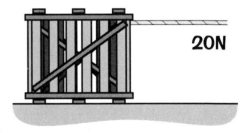

(a) How would your answers change if the crate was sliding with a constant speed of 1.2m/s? (That is, would the friction force be larger than, smaller than, or the same as before? Would the normal force be larger than, smaller than, or the same as before?) Explain.

(b) How would your answers change if the crate was sliding with a constant acceleration of 1.2m/s²?

(c) What assumptions did you make to answer part (b)?

R2. Is it possible to determine the force of kinetic friction without using its empirical force law? Explain. If it is possible, describe a situation in which it is true.

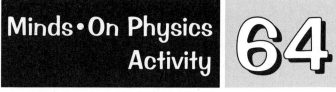
Calculating the Values of Physical Parameters and Quantities

Purpose and Expected Outcome

In this activity, you will learn how to determine the values of physical parameters (such as mass, spring constant, and shape parameter) and physical quantities (such as position, displacement, and velocity) using combinations of Newton's laws and the empirical force laws.

Prior Experience / Knowledge Needed

You should be familiar with all the common forces. You should know which forces obey empirical laws and when each empirical law can be used properly.

© 1999 Kendall/Hunt Publishing Company

Explanation of Activity and Example

Below are several physical situations. For each situation, one of the physical parameters (m, k, A, μ_k, or μ_s) or a physical quantity (x, Δx, v, or a) is <u>not</u> given, but there is enough information to find it. Use Newton's laws to determine the values of unknown forces, then use an empirical law to find the desired quantity. Use a value of $g = 10$N/kg throughout.

Example. A 40kg child stands on a 6kg swing as shown. The ropes supporting the swing behave like springs having spring constant 10,000N/m. How far do the ropes stretch from their relaxed state?

Answer: <u>*Each*</u> *rope stretches an amount, x = 2.3cm from its relaxed state.*

Explanation: All forces are vertical. The forces on the child are gravitation (400N down) and a normal force (400N up, given by Newton's 2nd law). The forces on the swing are a normal force (400N down, given by Newton's 3rd law), gravitation (60N down), and two tension forces (one due to each rope). If the tension forces are equal, then by Newton's 2nd law, each must be 230N. Treating the ropes like springs, the spring force is the tension force, or 230N. So, using the empirical law for the spring force, we find:

$$F_S = k\Delta x$$

$$230\text{N} = (10{,}000\text{N/m})\,\Delta x$$

$$\Delta x = 0.023\text{m} = 2.3\text{cm}$$

A1. A wooden crate is pulled at a constant speed of 2m/s along a horizontal surface by a rope having a tension of 40N. What is the coefficient of kinetic friction, μ_k?

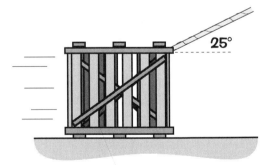

continued

A2. A cart is at rest on an incline as shown. The spring has a spring constant $k = 20$N/m and has been compressed 4cm from its relaxed position. What is the mass of the cart?

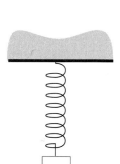

A3. An 80kg skydiver has a 10kg parachute (unopened on her back) and has reached a terminal velocity of 45m/s.

(a) What is the skydiver's shape parameter A?

(b) By changing to a horizontal position, the skydiver can quadruple her shape parameter. What is her maximum speed in this case?

(c) Opening her parachute changes her shape parameter by a factor of 50 (from its original value). What speed is she traveling just before hitting the ground? Would you consider this a safe speed to land? Explain.

A4. A series of masses are hung from a vertical spring and the length of the spring is measured in each case to the nearest millimeter. The data are shown below.

Hanging Mass	Length of Spring
50g	40.2cm
100g	45.8cm
150g	50.9cm
200g	56.4cm
250g	61.4cm
300g	66.9cm
350g	73.7cm
400g	81.2cm

(a) What is the spring constant for the spring?

(b) For what range of lengths does the spring behave like an ideal spring? Explain.

(c) What is the relaxed length of the spring? Explain.

(d) What would be the length of the spring if a mass of 500g were attached to it? Explain how you made your estimate.

Reflection

R1. For which of the situations in this activity did you use Newton's 2nd law to answer the questions? In each case, explain how you used Newton's 2nd law.

R2. For which situations in this activity did you use the empirical law for the gravitational force? Explain how. Was the goal in each case to determine the gravitational force, or something else? Explain.

R3. In problem A1, did you use one of Newton's laws or an empirical law to determine the friction force on the wooden crate? Explain.

R4. In problem A3, did you use Newton's laws or an empirical law to determine the force of air resistance on the skydiver? Explain.

Labeling Parts of Solutions and Executing Solution Plans

Purpose and Expected Outcome

Solving physics problems often involves the mathematical manipulation of many equations and formulas. Too often, students focus their attention on these formulas rather than the concepts, principles, and procedures used to solve problems. In this activity, you will learn more about the common concepts and procedures needed to solve most dynamics problems. After finishing this activity, you should be able to view a solution to a problem as a sequence of steps, each having a specific purpose and objective.

Prior Experience / Knowledge Needed

You should be familiar with kinematics, vectors, forces, free-body diagrams, and Newton's laws. In addition, you should have some experience solving problems using Newton's laws, especially the second law.

Explanation of Activity and Examples

There are two parts to this activity. In the first part, you are given complete solutions to problems, and you must label those parts of each solution that are indicated. In the second part, we present *solution plans*, which are descriptions of the steps used to solve problems and the reasons for doing each step. You are asked to solve each problem by following the steps of its solution plan.

PART A: Labeling Parts of a Solution

Each problem is accompanied by a worked-out solution. Within each solution, a number of quantities have been indicated using either a box or an arc. Describe each indicated item in the space provided. Examples have been provided for some of the parts.

A1. If you pushed a 20kg chair with a horizontal force of 160N, what would be the chair's acceleration, assuming that the friction force exerted on the chair is 80N?

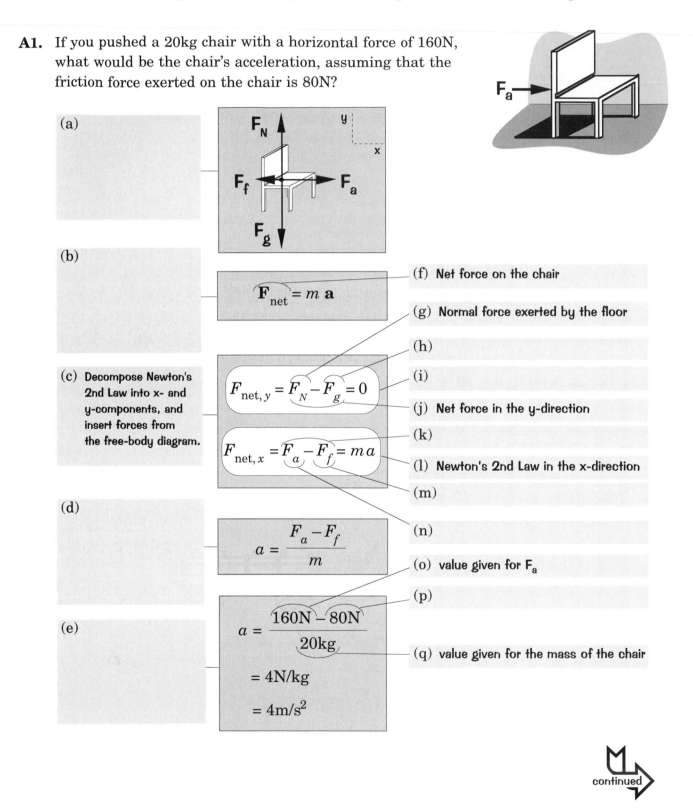

(a)

(b)

(c) Decompose Newton's 2nd Law into x- and y-components, and insert forces from the free-body diagram.

(d)

(e)

$$\mathbf{F}_{net} = m\,\mathbf{a}$$

$$F_{net,\,y} = F_N - F_g = 0$$

$$F_{net,\,x} = F_a - F_f = ma$$

$$a = \frac{F_a - F_f}{m}$$

$$a = \frac{160\text{N} - 80\text{N}}{20\text{kg}}$$

$$= 4\text{N/kg}$$

$$= 4\text{m/s}^2$$

(f) Net force on the chair

(g) Normal force exerted by the floor

(h)

(i)

(j) Net force in the y-direction

(k)

(l) Newton's 2nd Law in the x-direction

(m)

(n)

(o) value given for F_a

(p)

(q) value given for the mass of the chair

continued

A2. A car is parked on a hill when the brakes fail. How long does it take for the car to roll 100m down the hill? (Assume that the force of friction is about 600N and that the mass of the car is 1000kg.)

20°

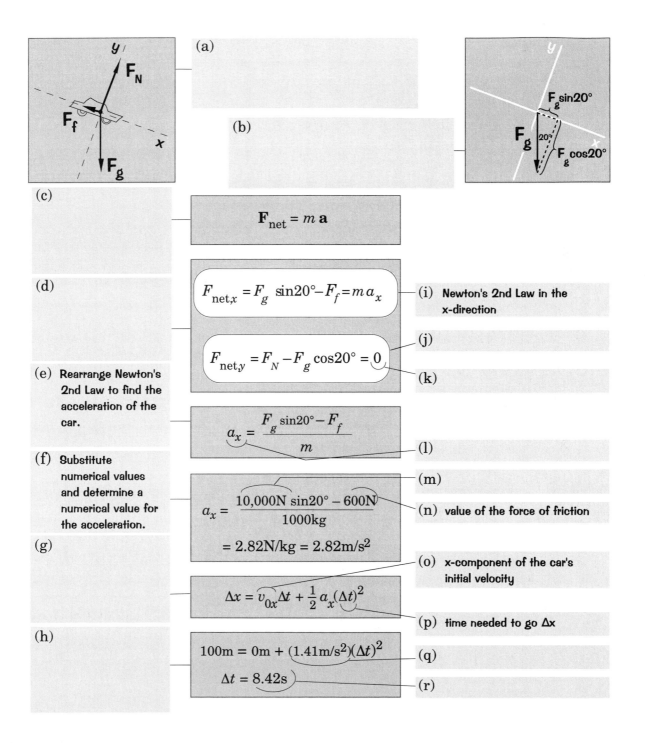

(a)

(b)

$F_g \sin 20°$

F_g 20°

$F_g \cos 20°$

(c)

$$\mathbf{F}_{net} = m\,\mathbf{a}$$

(d)

$$F_{net,x} = F_g \sin 20° - F_f = m\,a_x$$

(i) Newton's 2nd Law in the x-direction

(j)

$$F_{net,y} = F_N - F_g \cos 20° = 0$$

(k)

(e) Rearrange Newton's 2nd Law to find the acceleration of the car.

$$a_x = \frac{F_g \sin 20° - F_f}{m}$$

(l)

(f) Substitute numerical values and determine a numerical value for the acceleration.

(m)

$$a_x = \frac{10{,}000N \sin 20° - 600N}{1000kg}$$

(n) value of the force of friction

$$= 2.82N/kg = 2.82m/s^2$$

(g)

(o) x-component of the car's initial velocity

$$\Delta x = v_{0x}\Delta t + \frac{1}{2}a_x(\Delta t)^2$$

(p) time needed to go Δx

(h)

$$100m = 0m + (1.41m/s^2)(\Delta t)^2$$

(q)

$$\Delta t = 8.42s$$

(r)

PART B: Executing Solution Plans

A *Solution Plan* is a description of the steps needed to solve a problem and the reasons each step is needed or useful. Below are 3 problems, each with a Solution Plan. Follow the steps indicated and solve each problem.

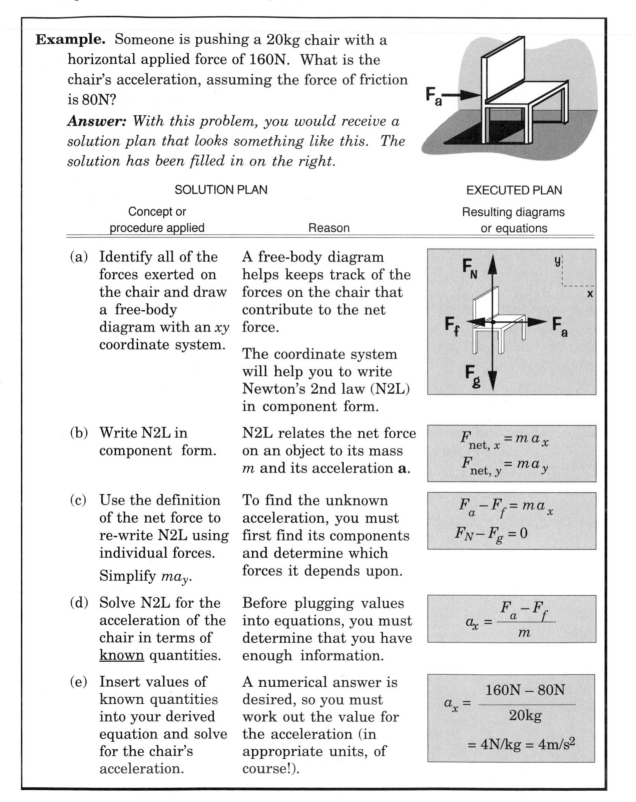

Example. Someone is pushing a 20kg chair with a horizontal applied force of 160N. What is the chair's acceleration, assuming the force of friction is 80N?

Answer: *With this problem, you would receive a solution plan that looks something like this. The solution has been filled in on the right.*

SOLUTION PLAN		EXECUTED PLAN
Concept or procedure applied	Reason	Resulting diagrams or equations
(a) Identify all of the forces exerted on the chair and draw a free-body diagram with an xy coordinate system.	A free-body diagram helps keeps track of the forces on the chair that contribute to the net force. The coordinate system will help you to write Newton's 2nd law (N2L) in component form.	
(b) Write N2L in component form.	N2L relates the net force on an object to its mass m and its acceleration **a**.	$F_{net,\,x} = m\,a_x$ $F_{net,\,y} = m\,a_y$
(c) Use the definition of the net force to re-write N2L using individual forces. Simplify ma_y.	To find the unknown acceleration, you must first find its components and determine which forces it depends upon.	$F_a - F_f = m\,a_x$ $F_N - F_g = 0$
(d) Solve N2L for the acceleration of the chair in terms of <u>known</u> quantities.	Before plugging values into equations, you must determine that you have enough information.	$a_x = \dfrac{F_a - F_f}{m}$
(e) Insert values of known quantities into your derived equation and solve for the chair's acceleration.	A numerical answer is desired, so you must work out the value for the acceleration (in appropriate units, of course!).	$a_x = \dfrac{160N - 80N}{20kg}$ $= 4N/kg = 4m/s^2$

B1. A construction worker lifts a bucket of cement from the ground to the roof of a building by means of a rope. If the mass of the bucket is 10kg, and the bucket moves with a constant speed of 2m/s, what is the tension force exerted by the rope on the bucket?

SOLUTION PLAN

Concept or procedure applied	Reason
(a) Identify all of the forces exerted on the bucket and draw a free-body diagram with an *xy* coordinate system.	A free-body diagram helps to keep track of the forces on the bucket that contribute to the net force. The coordinate system will help you to write Newton's 2nd law (N2L) in component form.
(b) Write Newton's 2nd law in component form.	N2L relates the net force on an object to its mass m and its acceleration **a**.
(c) Use the definition of net force to re-write N2L in the vertical direction (that is, the *y*-direction) only.	You do not need to consider the *x*-direction because all of the forces exerted on the bucket are in the vertical direction.
(d) Solve the previous equation for the tension force.	The tension force is the desired unknown.
(e) Determine the acceleration of the bucket. Use an empirical law to find the gravitational force on it.	Three quantities are needed to find the tension force, but only the mass is given. So, you must determine the other unknown quantities.
(f) Insert values of known quantities into your derived equation and solve for the tension force on the bucket.	A numerical answer is desired, so you must work out the value for the tension force (in appropriate units, of course!).

continued

B2. A 4kg box is dropped from a height of 25cm above a spring having spring constant 5N/cm. When the spring is compressed by 6cm, what is the acceleration of the box?

SOLUTION PLAN

Concept or procedure applied	Reason
(a) Identify all of the forces exerted on the box and draw a free-body diagram with an *xy* coordinate system.	A free-body diagram helps to keep track of the forces on the box that contribute to the net force. The coordinate system will help you to write Newton's 2nd law (N2L) in component form.
(b) Write Newton's 2nd law in component form.	N2L relates the net force on an object to its mass m and its acceleration **a**.
(c) Use the definition of net force to re-write N2L.	To find the acceleration, you must first determine which forces it depends upon.
(d) Solve the *y*-component of N2L for the acceleration of the box.	The acceleration is the desired unknown. There are no forces with horizontal components, so only the *y*-component needs to be considered.
(e) Insert empirical laws for the forces on the box.	You are not given any values for any of the forces, so you must determine them using other information.
(f) Substitute given values and solve for the acceleration of the box.	A numerical value is desired, so you must work out the value for the acceleration.

continued

B3. A 4kg box is pushed to the right with a force of 27N, while the small box next to it is pushed to the left. If there is no friction and the acceleration is observed to be 2.5m/s² to the right, what is the force exerted by the 4kg box on the smaller box?

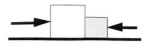

SOLUTION PLAN

Concept or procedure applied	Reason
(a) Identify all of the forces exerted on the 4kg box and draw a free-body diagram with an xy coordinate frame.	A free-body diagram helps to keep track of the forces on the 4kg box. The coordinate frame will help you to write Newton's 2nd law (N2L) in component form.
(b) Write Newton's 2nd law (in component form) for the 4kg box.	N2L relates the net force on an object to its mass m and its acceleration **a**.
(c) Re-write N2L in terms of the forces exerted on the 4kg box.	This will allow you to find the force exerted by the small box <u>on</u> the 4kg box.
(d) Solve the x-component of N2L for the force exerted on the 4kg box by the small box.	The desired unknown points horizontally, so only the x-component needs to be considered.
(e) Insert numerical values for the force exerted by the small box on the 4kg box and evaluate.	The value will be used to find the desired unknown.
(f) Apply Newton's 3rd law to the interaction between the two boxes.	This is the desired unknown.
(g) Combine the relations found in steps (e) and (f), and solve for the desired unknown. Be sure to indicate the direction of the unknown force.	A numerical value is desired for the force exerted by the 4kg box on the smaller box. Force is a vector quantity, so a direction must be specified.

Reflection

R1. Consider the problems in this activity. Fill in the table below by indicating <u>when</u> each of these general steps were used to solve each problem. (For instance, a free-body diagram was drawn during step (a) in A1 and B1.)

General steps for solving a problem		A1	A2	B1	B2	B3
i.	Draw a free-body diagram	a		a		
ii.	Find the components of a vector		b			
iii.	Apply Newton's 2nd law (N2L)	b		b		
iv.	Write N2L in component form		d			
v.	Use the definition of $\mathbf{F}_{net}$	c		c		
vi.	Use Newton's 3rd law		(−)			
vii.	Consider two different objects interacting	(−)				
viii.	Use kinematics to relate the position, velocity, and acceleration					
ix.	Use the definition of acceleration					
x.	Use an empirical force law					
xi.	Solve for the desired unknown					

R2. (a) Which of the steps listed above do you need to learn how to do better?

(b) Which of the steps do you feel as though you could help someone else to learn better?

R3. Consider problem B2. What direction is the acceleration of the box, up or down? Is the box speeding up or slowing down? Does this result surprise you? Resolve any inconsistencies between what you expect and what you determined for the direction of the acceleration.

R4. In problem B3, explain why it was not particularly useful to draw a free-body diagram for the small box.

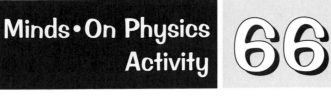
Developing Solution Plans and Solving Force Problems

Purpose and Expected Outcome

In the previous activity, you solved problems using solution plans that were given to you. In this activity, you will deepen your understanding of the steps needed to solve force problems, by writing your own solution plans. Then you will evaluate your problem-solving skills by analyzing and solving some problems on your own.

Prior Experience / Knowledge Needed

You should be familiar with kinematics, vectors, forces, free-body diagrams, and Newton's laws. In addition, you should have some experience with solution plans.

Explanation of Activity and Examples

There are two parts to this activity. In the first part, you are given complete solutions to problems, and you must write a description of the steps of each solution, along with the reasons for doing each step. In the second part, we present problems and encourage you to analyze each before diving into equations.

PART A: Developing a Solution Plan

Each problem in this part is accompanied by a worked-out solution. For each step in the solution, describe the concept or procedure used and state your reasons for using it. (For A2, you must fill in some of the steps as well.)

A1. A child is walking along the sidewalk at a speed of 1m/s while pulling his dog sitting in a wagon. The dog has a mass of 30kg, and the wagon weighs 50N. If the childs pulls at an angle of 12°, and the frictional force exerted on the wagon by the ground is 60N, then how hard does the child pull on the handle?

EXECUTED PLAN	EXECUTED PLAN
Resulting diagrams or equations	(continued)

(a)

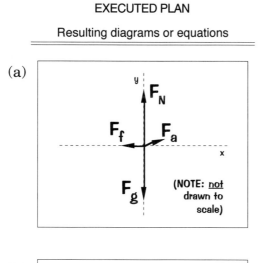

(NOTE: <u>not</u> drawn to scale)

(b)
$$F_{net,\,x} = ma_x$$
$$F_{net,\,y} = ma_y$$

(c)
$$F_a \cos 12° - F_f = 0$$
$$F_N + F_a \sin 12° - F_g = 0$$

(d)
$$F_a = \frac{F_f}{\cos 12°}$$

(e)
$$F_a = \frac{60\text{N}}{0.978}$$
$$= 61.3\text{N}$$

continued

A2. A child slides a 40g cookie across the floor. The cookie starts out with a speed of 2m/s and stops 3s later. What is the frictional force on the cookie? (**Note:** For this problem, you must fill in the missing diagrams and equations in addition to writing a Solution Plan.)

EXECUTED PLAN

Resulting diagrams or equations

(a)
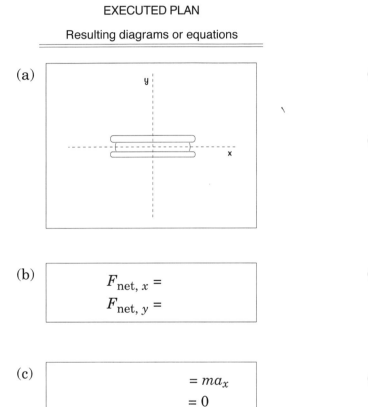

(b)
$$F_{net, x} =$$
$$F_{net, y} =$$

(c)
$$= ma_x$$
$$= 0$$

EXECUTED PLAN

(continued)

(d)
$$F_f =$$

(e)
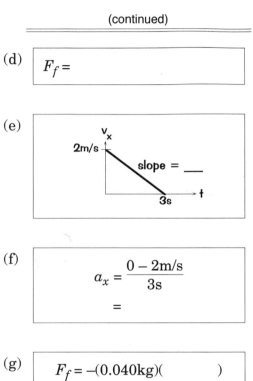

(f)
$$a_x = \frac{0 - 2\text{m/s}}{3\text{s}}$$
$$=$$

(g)
$$F_f = -(0.040\text{kg})(\qquad)$$
$$=$$
$$=$$

PART B: Solving Force Problems

Now that you have worked on developing all of the skills needed to solve problems, you can find out how well you can actually solve them. Keep in mind the concepts and procedures you have been using to analyze problem situations, and use them here to make sure the equations you use are appropriate to each situation. Think about <u>how</u> you will solve each problem before solving it.

B1. A child is walking along the sidewalk at a speed of 1m/s while pulling his dog sitting in a wagon. The dog has a mass of 30kg, and the wagon weighs 50N. If the child pulls at an angle of 12°, and the frictional force exerted on the wagon by the ground is 60N, then what is the frictional force exerted by the wagon on the dog?

B2. A child slides a 40g cookie across the floor. The cookie starts out with a speed of 2m/s and stops 3s later. What is the coefficient of friction between the cookie and the floor?

B3. A construction worker lifts a bucket of cement from the ground to the roof of a building by means of a rope. If the mass of the bucket is 10kg, and the bucket is accelerating (briefly) at 2m/s², what is the tension force exerted by the rope on the bucket?

B4. A tow truck is pushing a car to a nearby service station at about 35 miles per hour (almost 16m/s). The shape parameter for the car is about 3Ns²/m². If the front bumper of the tow truck is compressed about 2cm, estimate its spring constant.

Reflection

R1. For each of the problems in part B, indicate (a) which forces you determined using an empirical law, (b) which forces you determined using Newton's 2nd law, and (c) which forces you determined using Newton's 3rd law.

R2. When an object is moving in a straight line, what is the component of acceleration perpendicular to the motion. Describe two examples.

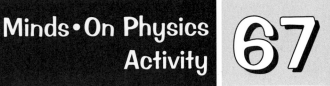

Solving Force Problems:
Reflection and Integration

Purpose and Expected Outcome

There are many different types of relationships used to understand dynamics and solve force problems. In this activity, you will learn to classify those relationships.

Prior Experience / Knowledge Needed

You should know kinematics, the force laws, Newton's laws, and how all of them are related. You should know how to solve problems using Newton's laws.

Explanation of Activity

There are two parts in this activity. In the first part, you will explore the differences between *definitions*, *empirical force laws*, *dynamical laws*, and *mathematical principles*. In the second part you will define what is meant by *definitions*, *empirical laws*, *dynamical laws*, and *derived relations*.

PART A: Classifying Relationships Used in Dynamics

Fill in the following tables.

A1. List the <u>definitions</u> that you have learned so far, and provide a short description of each. If possible, also provide a mathematical description of each. (Some examples have been given.)

	Definitions	Short Description	Mathematical Description
(a)	Displacement		
(b)	Average velocity		
(c)			$\Delta \mathbf{x}/\Delta t$ (Δt small)
(d)			$\Delta \mathbf{v}/\Delta t$
(e)		rate at which the velocity is changing	
(f)	Net force		

A2. List the <u>empirical force laws</u> that you have learned and used so far, and provide a short description of each. If possible, also provide a mathematical description of each. (Some examples have been given.)

	Empirical Force Laws	Short Description	Mathematical Description
(a)			$F_g = mg$
(b)		proportional to the change in length of the spring from its relaxed state	
(c)	Frictional (two types)		
(d)		proportional to the squared speed of an object relative to its surroundings	

continued

A3. List the <u>dynamical laws</u> that you have learned so far, and provide a short description of each. If possible, provide a mathematical description of each.

Dynamical Laws	Short Description	Mathematical Description
(a)		
(b)	The net force on an object is equal to its mass multiplied by its acceleration.	
(c) Newton's 3rd law		

A4. List the <u>mathematical principles</u> that you have learned so far.

   (a) The slope of position vs. time at any particular time is equal to the _____ of the object at the same time.

   (b) The slope of _____ at any particular time is equal to the _____ of the object at the same time.

   (c) The area below _____ between two times is the change in velocity of the object.

   (d) The area below _____ between two times is the change in _____ of the object.

Summary

Most, but not all, of the relationships you have learned and have been using appear in one of the four categories listed above. The missing relationships are the ones you derived for the position and velocity of an object experiencing constant acceleration, which are derived from the definitions of position and velocity.

As we continue to present new ideas and relationships, you should determine and take note of which category each belongs in. Is it a definition? Or is it an empirical law? Or a dynamical law? Or just a derived relation? This will help you to remember them and distinguish them from each other. It will also help you to apply them properly to new situations.

PART B: Describing Relationships Used in Dynamics

For each of the descriptions below, indicate the category (A, B, C or D) that is being described:

A. Definitions

B. Empirical Laws

C. Dynamical Laws

D. Derived Relations

_____ **B1.** Relationships that indicate how an object or system of objects reacts to forces. These can sometimes be verified experimentally.

_____ **B2.** Relationships derived through experimentation and observation.

_____ **B3.** Relationships determined using other (more fundamental) relationships.

_____ **B4.** Relationships used to introduce new ideas and concepts. These usually involve a new symbol which is defined in terms of previously defined symbols.

Summarizing and Structuring Dynamics

Purpose and Expected Outcome

You have finished dynamics. To help you learn how to use dynamics to understand physical situations and solve problems, you must organize what you know, and see how it fits together. In this activity, you will list the important ideas within dynamics and learn how they are related to each other. You will also add items to your list of problem-solving techniques and categorize them.

Prior Experience / Knowledge Needed

You should know kinematics, the force laws, Newton's laws, and how all of them are related. You should know how to solve problems using Newton's laws.

Explanation of Activity

There are three parts to this activity.

PART A: Summarizing Forces

Review the tables you made for kinematics and for interactions. On a separate sheet of paper, make a list of any important ideas not yet defined (such as *net force*, *mass*, and *equilibrium*) and describe each one using words and equations. Then list Newton's laws, describe each one using words and / or equations, and explain the significance of each one.

PART B: Making a Concept Map

Working in a small group or as a class, organize the entries from all your tables and arrange them into a concept map of kinematics, interactions, and dynamics. Your diagram should contain <u>at least</u> the following:

- Newton's laws
- free-body diagram
- net force
- mass
- position, velocity, acceleration, and displacement
- examples of common forces

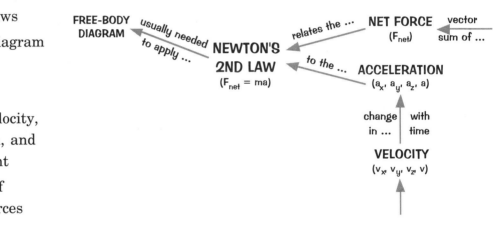

PART C: Listing Problem-Solving Ideas

As a class, update your list of problem-solving ideas. (You might find it useful and helpful to review some of the Reflection questions from the last few activities.) Consider all the items in your list and sort them into two categories:

(1) *General techniques.* These are good procedures and tactics that apply to <u>all</u> problems, such as "Check your math", "Consider a different representation of the problem or solution", and "Show all your work".

(2) *Specialized techniques.* These are problem-solving ideas that are important only for a particular kind of problem. For example, "Indicate coordinate axes on a free-body diagram" is useful primarily for dynamics problems. "Check to see if air resistance is negligible" is not always used either.

Going Beyond
Newton's Laws

Purpose and Expected Outcome

To date, the MOP activities have explored a wide variety of situations and ideas. After each activity, we have asked you to reflect on what you did during the activity. This is intended to help you gain a deeper understanding of the ideas used in the activity. Now that you have finished dynamics, it is especially important to look back at everything you have done so far. What can you do with dynamics and kinematics? (Quite a bit!) And what can you <u>not</u> do with dynamics? (Quite a bit more!!) In this activity, you will learn to recognize those problem situations for which dynamics and kinematics can be applied, and to distinguish them from situations for which dynamics and kinematics <u>cannot</u> be applied.

Prior Experience / Knowledge Needed

You should know kinematics. You should know Newton's laws and be able to apply them to reasoning and to problem-solving situations. You should be able to describe and explain the problem-solving approach represented in the diagram below. Many (but not all) dynamics problems are solved using the three steps described here.

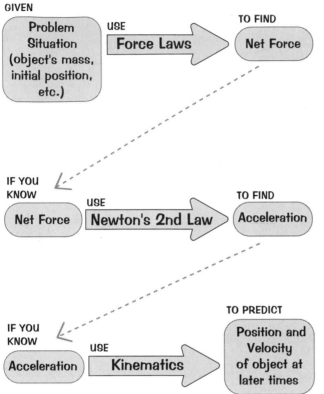

Step 1: If you are given enough information about the problem situation, such as the masses of objects, initial positions and velocities, coefficients of friction, and spring constants, you can use empirical force laws to determine the net force exerted on particular objects.

Step 2: If you know the net force exerted on an object and its mass, you can use Newton's second law to find its acceleration.

Step 3: If you know the acceleration of an object, as well as its initial position and velocity, you can use kinematics to determine where it will be, how fast it is moving, and its direction of motion at later times.

Explanation of Activity

Described below are 6 problems. For each one, (a) decide whether or not you can solve the problem using the three steps shown above. Then, for those problems you <u>cannot</u> solve, (b) identify the step (1, 2, or 3) that cannot be taken and (c) explain why it cannot. **Note:** Do <u>not</u> solve these problems.

A1. A 1kg cart is released from rest on a 5° inclined plane. Determine its position $\frac{1}{2}$ second later.

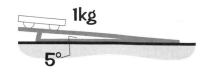

    (a) Can you use the three steps above to solve this problem?

    (b) If not, which step (1, 2 or 3) cannot be followed?

    (c) Explain.

A2. A cart rolls down a small hill, starting from rest. Find the cart's velocity when it reaches the bottom of the hill.

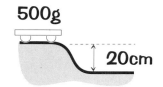

    (a) Can you use the three steps above to solve this problem?

    (b) If not, which step cannot be followed?

    (c) Explain.

A3. A book slides along the floor, eventually coming to a stop. Write an expression for its position as a function of time.

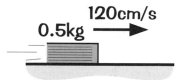

    (a) Can you use the three steps above to solve this problem?

    (b) If not, which step cannot be followed?

    (c) Explain.

A4. A wagon is pulled by a rope having constant tension. What is the wagon's velocity at $t = 3$s?

    (a) Can you use the three steps above to solve this problem?

    (b) If not, which step cannot be followed?

    (c) Explain.

continued

A5. A 100g ball is attached to a string and released from rest as shown. Determine the ball's velocity when it is at the bottom of its swing.

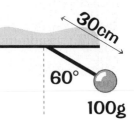

(a) Can you use the three steps above to solve this problem?

(b) If not, which step cannot be followed?

(c) Explain.

A6. A 1kg cart compresses a 10N/cm spring by 5cm and is released from rest. When will the cart lose contact with the spring?

(a) Can you use the three steps above to solve this problem?

(b) If not, which step cannot be followed?

(c) Explain.

Reflection

R1. Reconsider situation A1.

(a) If you were not given the cart's mass, would you be able to solve the problem? Explain.

(b) What if you were not given the angle? Explain.

R2. What must be true about the acceleration of an object in order for <u>you</u> to be able to predict its velocity at a later time?

R3. (a) For which situations do you know the net force as a function of <u>position</u>?

(b) For which situations do you know the net force as a function of <u>time</u>?

(c) Which is needed for you to solve problems using dynamics? Explain.

R4. Discuss the virtues and limitations of dynamics for solving problems.

Looking for New Principles

Purpose and Expected Outcome

Having established that dynamics cannot be used to solve all problems, we would like to find other physical principles to help us understand situations better. In this hands-on activity, you will explore a variety of situations, some of which have definite patterns, and some of which do not. Even though you will be able to use dynamics to understand the <u>qualitative</u> features of these situations, you will find that dynamics <u>cannot</u> be used to actually predict the positions and velocities of objects.

Prior Experience / Knowledge Needed

You should know Newton's laws and be able to use them to understand qualitatively the motion of objects interacting with each other. You should be familiar with the limitations of dynamics for solving problems, as well as some of the reasons dynamics is limited.

Explanation of Activity

There are two parts to this activity, both of which are to be done <u>hands-on</u>.

PART A: Exploring the Motion of Two Interacting Objects

For each situation below, arrange the items as needed and consider two objects interacting with each other.

A1. Two equal-mass carts collide with a spring-loaded bumper between them. Cart A (on the left) moves to the right before the collision, and cart B (on the right) is at rest. Note carefully the locations of the moveable weights on each of the carts.

(a) Sketch a graph of the net force on each cart versus time. How long do you suppose the two carts are in contact? (Make a guess.)

(b) Can you use Newton's laws to predict the motion of the two carts? Explain why or why not.

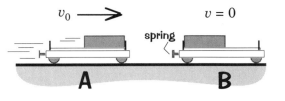

A2. Two identical steel balls are attached to identical strings and connected to the ceiling (or other horizontal support) so that they are <u>just</u> touching when they are hanging at rest. One of the balls is pulled to the side and released from rest.

(a) Sketch a graph of the net force on each steel ball versus time during the collision. How long do you suppose the two balls are in contact? (Guess.)

(b) Can you use Newton's laws to predict the motion of the two steel balls as a result of the collision? Explain why or why not.

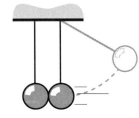

(c) How is the motion of the two steel balls in this situation similar to the motion of the two carts in A1? What physical characteristics of the situations do you suppose leads to this similarity?

A3. This is the same as situation A1, except that the weight on cart B has been moved to the right side of the cart.

(a) Sketch a graph of the net force on each cart versus time. Is this graph the same as the one you made for situation A1? Explain why or why not.

(b) Is the force law (spring force versus position) in this situation the same as the force law in situation A1? Explain why or why not.

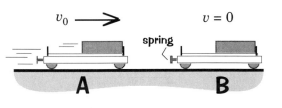

(c) How is the motion of the two carts in this situation different from the motion of the two carts in A1? What physical characteristics of the situations do you suppose lead to this difference? Explain.

Summary of Part A

In A1 and A3, we know the force law, but we cannot predict the motion of the carts, because we do not know how the net force changes with <u>time</u>. In A2, we do not even know the force law governing the motion of the balls. It probably has something to do with the materials used to make the balls, but that does not help us here. Even though we cannot predict the behavior of the colliding objects using Newton's laws, something predictable is happening. After the collisions in both A1 and A2, the moving object stopped and the stationary object moved with the same velocity as the moving object. In fact, for different initial speeds of the moving objects, the same result would occur. This is our first clue that a new pattern or principle is emerging, separate from dynamics.

Comparing A1 and A3, we learn that rigid objects behave differently than objects with moving parts. Without changing anything else from A1—even the force law is the same—the location of the weight in A3 changed the situation enough to alter the behavior of both carts after the collision. Although the behavior is complicated, we will find that two things (called *momentum* and *energy*) stay the same throughout the interaction between the two carts in both cases.

PART B: Exploring More Complicated Situations

For each of the situations described below, arrange the items as needed, then make careful observations and look for regular patterns of behavior.

B1. Five steel balls are arranged on a rigid support as shown. Each ball should hang perfectly vertical when at rest and also be in contact with each of its neighbors.

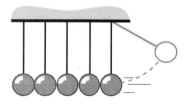

(a) Pull one of the balls to the side and release it from rest. Describe what happens as a result of the collision? How does your result depend upon the initial height of the "first" ball? How does the final height of the "other" ball compare to the initial height of the first ball?

(b) Try other combinations, such as pulling two or three balls to one side, or pulling one ball from each end, and release them from rest at the same instant. In each case, describe what happens as a result of the collision.

(c) Describe any patterns you perceive in the behavior of the balls in this arrangement.

(d) Consider an arrangement you have <u>not</u> tried already, such as pulling two balls from one side and one ball from the other, and predict what you believe will happen when they are released from rest. What general rule can you give that would allow someone to predict the behavior for any combination?

continued

B2. A ball is connected to one end of a string, whose other end is connected to a horizontal string as shown. Later, a second and third ball are added to the string. All three balls should be identical to each other, and the vertical strings should all be the same length. The balls should <u>not</u> touch when they are hanging vertically at rest. Leave plenty of space between balls, so that they can pass by each other easily as they swing forward and backward (perpendicular to the paper).

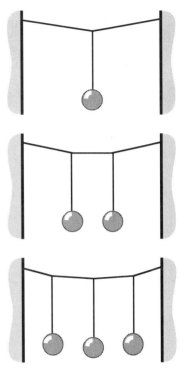

(a) Start with just one ball connected to the string. Pull the ball forward and release it from rest. Observe its motion for several cycles. Sketch a graph of its speed versus time. Also sketch a graph of its height versus time, using its lowest position as a reference height. What is the <u>qualitative</u> relationship between the speed of the ball and its height? Can you predict the times at which the ball is at rest? Explain why or why not.

(b) Now add a second ball as shown. Pull <u>one</u> of the balls forward and release it from rest. Sketch a graph of the speed of each ball versus time. Use the same set of axes for both graphs, and make sure each graph is clearly labeled. Which ball appears to be moving more of the time, or is the motion of the two balls similar? Explain the relationship between the speeds of the two balls. Is there a pattern to the behavior of this system? If so, what is it? Based on your observation so far, can you predict the times when one of the balls is hanging vertically and is at rest? How?

(c) Add a third ball to the arrangement. Pull one ball forward and release it from rest. Sketch a graph of the speed of the "first" ball versus time. Is there a pattern to the behavior of this system? If so, what is it? Could you predict the speed of any one of the balls at some later time? Explain why or why not.

(d) How does the motion of any one ball change as more balls are added to the arrangement? (Consider in particular: the maximum speed of any one ball, the maximum height of any one ball, and the overall pattern.) What do you think would happen if a large number of balls were used?

Summary of Part B

When there is only one ball connected to a string, the motion is relatively simple and repetitive. Also, there is a close relationship between the speed of the ball and its height: When the ball is at its lowest point, it is moving fastest, and when it is at its highest point, it stops. You will learn that *energy* ideas allow you to predict the maximum speed of the ball given its maximum height and vice versa. Also, the time needed for the ball to complete one cycle stays the same, so we can predict the times at which the ball stops.

When we add a 2nd ball, the motion is a bit more complicated, but some patterns remain. First one ball swings maximally, while the other is at rest. Then the other swings maximally, while the first is at rest. The time required to complete one of these cycles is longer than the time for each individual swing, but the time seems to stay roughly constant. This means we can predict when each ball is hanging vertically and is at rest.

Based on our observations of three balls, we can predict that the larger the number of balls, the more difficult it is to keep track of individual balls and to perceive patterns. The motion seems to be more random, and the motion also seems to be more evenly distributed throughout the system. This suggest that "something" is shared. We will find that it is *energy* that is shared by the objects in the system.

Reflection

R1. In which situations did you expect the behavior you observed? Was it because you had seen it before, or because you had seen something <u>like</u> it before, or something else? Explain.

R2. In which situations were you surprised by the behavior you observed? What was most surprising about each of them? What had you expected before you saw it? Think about experiences you have had before doing this activity. For each surprising result, give an example of something you have previously experienced that is like what you observed here.

Integration of Ideas

In upcoming activities, you will explore two new ideas that are extremely useful for understanding the behavior of systems. They are *momentum* and *energy*. We will find that momentum and energy can never by "created" or "destroyed", but always stays the same. If one object "gains" momentum or energy, then another object must "lose" the same amount. When the amount of something stays the same, we say it is *conserved*.

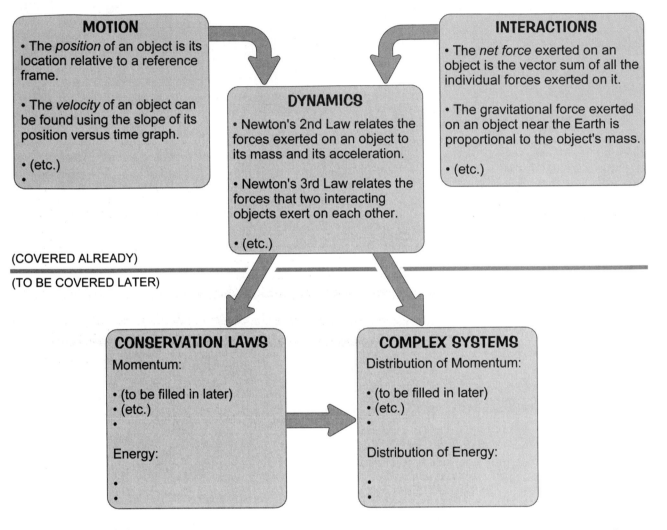

The diagram above shows the structure of the topics you have covered so far, and their relationship to topics you will soon learn about. You have already summarized the main ideas within Motion, Interactions, and Dynamics. As you learn about Momentum and Energy, keep in mind that you will soon be filling in this structure. Then we will move on to Complex Systems, and see how momentum and energy are distributed within different systems.

Reader

Chapter 2:
DESCRIBING
INTERACTIONS

— and —

Appendix:
TABLE OF
COMMON
FORCES

DESCRIBING INTERACTIONS

Introduction. *Dynamics* is the study of how objects affect the motion of other objects through *interactions*. The way in which one object influences the motion of another object involves the idea of a *force*, and the response of the object is often characterized by a change in velocity (that is, an acceleration). This is why we have spent so much time thus far helping you to develop your ideas about acceleration. Now we will learn about what causes something to accelerate. We will also explain how interactions can be present even when something is <u>not</u> accelerating.

2.1   INTERACTIONS AND FORCES

Interactions. When two objects influence each other, we say that they are *interacting*. Depending on the circumstances, the effect of the interaction might be:

- the motion of one or both objects is changed in some way (speeding up, slowing down, changing direction, etc.)

- the shape of one or both objects changes, such as when a spring is compressed.

Sometimes neither effect is visible, such as when a glass is sitting at rest on a table top. However, we can say that the motion is different from what we would expect if the table were not there. In other words, without the table, the glass would fall; therefore the motion of the glass is certainly affected by the table. In fact, though we cannot see it for ourselves, the positions of the atoms on the surface of the table are certainly affected by the glass sitting on it. So, the shape of the table changes, though microscopically. Therefore, we can say that the glass and the table are interacting. An *inter*action is always two-way—always between "object *A*" and "object *B*". (You should be able to identify the two objects.)

Forces. Whenever two objects interact, we say that each exerts a *force* on the other. A force consists of two parts: (1) how strongly each object influences the other, <u>and</u> (2) the direction of the influence. (Force is a vector quantity, so it has both a magnitude and a direction.)

We have many different ways of saying that two objects influence each other, all of which are equivalent. For example:

- *There is an interaction between this object and that object.*

- *These two objects are interacting with each other.*

- *These two objects act on each other.*

- *Each of these two objects exerts a force on the other.*

- *Object A exerts a force on object B, <u>and</u> object B exerts a force on object A.*

All of these statements are just different ways of saying the same thing. For example, when you throw a ball, *there is an interaction between* the ball *and* your hand. The hand *exerts a force on* the ball, setting the ball in motion, and the ball *exerts a force on* the hand, which you can feel, either because your skin is compressed or because your fingers are bent backwards.

When something interacts with <u>you</u>, you might feel pushed or pulled by it. The force tells you how strong the push or pull feels at any particular instant of time. (The force also tells you the direction.) The force can be different at different instants. Imagine giving something a push in slow motion. You might be aware of pushing less hard at the beginning of the push, pushing hardest in the middle of the push, and then pushing less hard again at the end. Or imagine swinging a ball on a string in a large circle. As you are swinging the ball, the direction of the force on it is constantly changing. The total effect of a push (or pull, or combination of both) is called an *impulse*, which we will introduce later in the course.

Measuring forces. Because interactions affect the shape of many objects, we have a way of measuring forces. Springs are easily stretched or compressed, so we often use a spring scale to measure the magnitude of a force being exerted on an object. Platform scales (such as a typical bathroom scale) use springs that are compressed rather than stretched. In general, before using a spring scale, we need to make sure we know what it is we are measuring with it. For example, if someone pushes down on your shoulders while you are standing on a bathroom scale, the scale will not read your weight, but a value slightly larger. Scales are usually calibrated so that the distance the spring stretches or compresses is proportional to the magnitude of the force exerted on it.

Units of force. The unit of force most commonly used in the United States is the *pound* (lb). In the metric (SI) system, the proper unit of force is the *newton* (N). One pound is just less than $4\frac{1}{2}$ newtons; one newton is a little less than $1/4$ pound. (More precisely, 1lb = 4.45N, so 1N = 0.225lb.) Convert your own weight (in lbs) to newtons. Remembering your weight in both pounds and newtons will give you a stronger sense of how *small* a newton is. (For instance, go tell a classmate that he or she weighs over 500 newtons, and see what he or she thinks about that!)

Identifying forces. A force is one side of an interaction between two objects. To identify force, you must:

Identify both interacting objects. You can usually identify the interaction pair by answering questions such as "What is exerting the force?" and "What is the force being exerted on?"

Identify the kind of force or interaction. There are two main categories for forces: (1) Contact forces are those that require two objects to be touching. Examples are the spring force and the friction force. (2) Action-at-a-distance forces are those that do not require contact (touching each other), such as the electric force, the magnetic force, and the gravitational force.

Within these two categories, there are many different types of forces. Most of the everyday forces are listed in the Table of Common Forces found in the Appendix (starting after page R60). In this table you will find:

- a description of each force, telling you what factors affect the magnitude and direction of the force, and what kinds of objects usually cause it to be present;

- guidelines for determining when each force is present and when each can be neglected or ignored; and

- (if possible) a force law or relationship that allows you to calculate the value of each force when you know certain information about the situation.

It is important for you to familiarize yourself with a variety of example situations to help you understand when a particular kind of force is present and when it is not. Most forces require contact: In most cases, two objects must be touching each other in order for them to exert forces on each other. No contact; no force. For example, the force that your hand exerts on a ball is no longer there as soon as the ball leaves your hand. The only exceptions (that will be considered this year) are the gravitational, magnetic, and electrostatic forces.

Contact alone is not enough to guarantee that a force will be exerted. For example, when a spring is attached to something, but remains unstretched and uncompressed, it exerts no force on the object it is touching. When a book is sitting on a table, there is no friction force exerted on it. When a string is attached to something, it must be *taut* in order for a tension force to be exerted. A *slack* string exerts no force.

The following examples show situations in which some of the common forces are exerted and similar situations in which they are not.

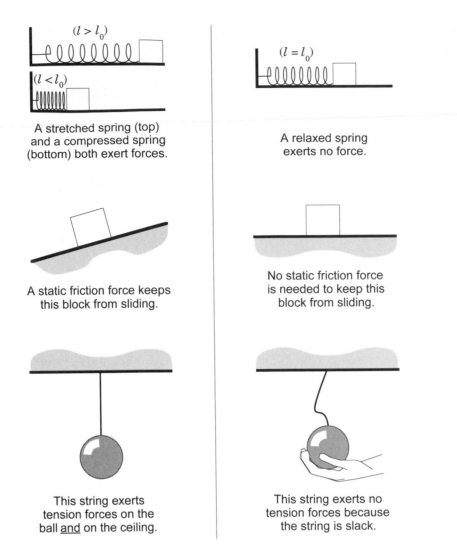

A stretched spring (top) and a compressed spring (bottom) both exert forces.

A relaxed spring exerts no force.

A static friction force keeps this block from sliding.

No static friction force is needed to keep this block from sliding.

This string exerts tension forces on the ball <u>and</u> on the ceiling.

This string exerts no tension forces because the string is slack.

**situations in which particular forces
are exerted (left) and are not exerted (right)**

It is important also to know how to find the <u>direction</u> of any particular force. For example, the normal force always points directly away from the surface exerting the force, as shown below.

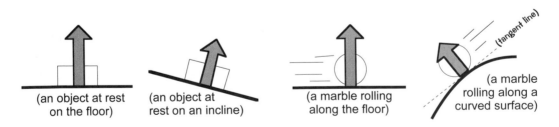

(an object at rest on the floor)

(an object at rest on an incline)

(a marble rolling along the floor)

(tangent line)

(a marble rolling along a curved surface)

four situations showing the direction of the normal force

The direction of a spring force is always opposite to the displacement of the end of the spring from its relaxed position. In the examples below, the displacement of the end of the spring is represented by a small white arrow, and the direction of the spring force is represented by a large gray arrow. The direction of the spring force has nothing to do with the motion of the object. Rather, its direction is always along the axis of the spring.

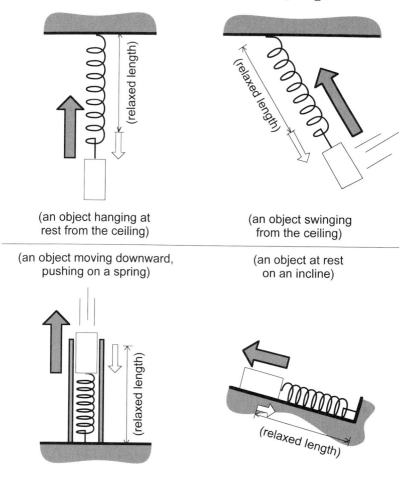

(an object hanging at
rest from the ceiling)

(an object swinging
from the ceiling)

(an object moving downward,
pushing on a spring)

(an object at rest
on an incline)

four situations showing the direction of the spring force

Empirical force laws. Many common forces can be represented by a mathematical expression called an *empirical force law*. *Empirical* means that the relationship is determined or was discovered by doing an experiment. Each empirical law depends upon a proportionality constant, such as k for springs, g for gravitation (near the surface of a celestial object), and μ_k for kinetic friction. Each law also depends upon one or more physical features or quantities, such as the mass m or the speed v of an object, or the length l of a spring. In the table below, we present each of the empirical force laws, with a brief description of the factors that affect each.

Note that the equations listed below can be used only to find the <u>magnitude</u> of these forces. As discussed previously, to use the empirical force laws, you must also know how to find the directions of these forces.

Table I. Summary of the Empirical Laws for Common Forces

...of	symbol	Proportionality Constant (units)	symbol	Physical Feature (units)	symbol	Empirical Law
...ng force ...lso called ...lastic force)	F_s	Spring constant. (N/cm)	k	Length of spring. (cm) Relaxed length. (cm)	l l_0	$F_s = k\,\lvert l - l_0 \rvert$
Gravitational force (near the surface of the earth)	F_g	Gravitational constant. (N/kg)	g	Mass. (kg)	m	$F_g = mg$
Kinetic friction force	F_{fk}	Coefficient of kinetic friction. (dimensionless)	μ_k	Normal force exerted on object. (newtons)	F_N	$F_{fk} = \mu_k F_N$
Static friction force (maximum value only)	F_{fs}	Coefficient of static friction. (dimensionless)	μ_s	Normal force exerted on object. (newtons)	F_N	$F_{fs} \le \mu_s F_N$ — or — $F_{fs,\text{max}} = \mu_s F_N$
Air resistance force (also called Drag force)	F_{air}	Shape parameter. (N-s^2/m^2)	A	Speed. (m/s)	v	$F_{air} = Av^2$

Fundamental laws for forces versus empirical laws. At the most basic level (that is, microscopic), all interactions in nature are between subatomic particles, like electrons and protons. The force laws describing how these particles interact are called *fundamental force laws*. In practice, it is nearly impossible to use these force laws to describe how large-scale objects—such as springs, strings, blocks, cars, etc.—interact with each other. We just do not know how to solve problems involving that many subatomic particles!

Instead, scientists do experiments to see how the empirical forces (the combined effect of all the microscopic forces) behave in various situations. First, they determine what features are

most relevant, such as the mass of an object or the displacement of the end of a spring. T[   ]
they determine exactly how the force is affected by the relevant features. If possible, this
process yields a relationship that allows us to calculate the value of a force over a wide ran[ ]
of conditions. However, there is usually a limit to this range. For example, *Hooke's Law*,
which gives the force exerted by a spring, applies only if the spring is not stretched or
compressed too far from its relaxed length. Every spring has its own characteristic constant k
But if someone <u>permanently</u> deforms the spring, the spring constant also changes!
(Permanently!)

Fundamental laws for forces. In this course, we will present only two of the fundamental
force laws, one for the gravitational force and one for the electrical force. They are shown in
the table below. Each one assumes that the objects are point particles. Although you will not
be dealing with either one of these for quite some time, you should note the similarity in the
<u>form</u> of these two relationships.

Table II. Summary of the Fundamental Laws for Two Common Forces

Force	symbol	Proportionality Constant (units)	symbol	Physical Feature (units)	symbol	Force Law[*]
Gravitational force	F_g	Universal gravitational constant. $(N\text{-}m^2/kg^2)$	G	Masses of the two objects interacting. (kg)	m_1 m_2	$F_g = G\dfrac{m_1 m_2}{r^2}$
(valid at all distances, but valid only for point particles)				Separation of the two objects interacting. (m)	r	
Electric force (or Coulomb force)	F_c	Universal electrical constant. $(N\text{-}m^2/C^2)$	k	Charges of the two objects interacting. (C)	q_1 q_2	$F_c = k\dfrac{q_1 q_2}{r^2}$
(valid at all distances, but valid only for point particles in a vacuum)				Separation of the two objects interacting. (m)	r	

[*]To find the directions of these forces, see pages A5 and A6 in the Table of Common Forces.

Freebody diagrams: A way to help us inventory forces. To begin to understand how an object's motion is affected by the forces exerted on it, we must identify all the forces that contribute to the combined effect. A *free-body diagram* is an excellent way of presenting a "picture" of an object's force situation. A free-body diagram shows <u>all</u> the forces exerted on a single, isolated object (called the "free body"). The idea is that we <u>remove</u> everything interacting with our object, and <u>replace</u> their effect with the forces they exert. This is because the motion of our object is completely determined by the forces exerted on it. So the motion of the free body (with the particular set of forces exerted on it) is the same as the motion of the "real" object.

Some valid free-body diagrams are shown below.

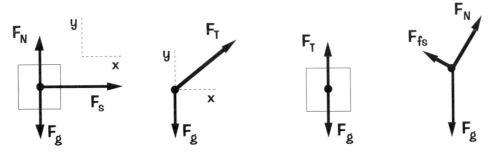

some valid free-body diagrams

By convention, in order to reduce confusion and the possibility for error, we follow these rules for drawing valid free-body diagrams:

- <u>Only forces</u> (not velocities, accelerations, or the net force) should be put onto a free-body diagram.

- <u>All</u> the forces exerted on the object are put onto the diagram, but

- <u>None</u> of the objects exerting those forces are put onto the diagram.

- We usually use a <u>point</u> to represent the "free" body. (We can use a point to represent the body whenever we can consider it a *point object*, in other words, whenever it does not matter where on the object a force is exerted. For example, if we only care about the overall falling motion of a diver going off a high board, and we are not interested in the different paths followed by her head and her feet as she rotates in the air, then we can represent her as a point object.) <u>All</u> forces start from this point, and this point is placed <u>away</u> from all other diagrams and illustrations.

- Each force is represented by a *directed line segment* (an arrow; a straight line with an arrowhead on one end). The tail end of the arrow is placed at the point representing the object. The direction of the arrow is the same as the direction of the force. Whenever possible, the length of each arrow should be roughly proportional to the magnitude of the force it represents.

- Each force is <u>clearly labeled</u> and distinguishable from all the other forces exerted in the physical situation.

And there are also two <u>optional</u> features:

- A sketch of the object <u>might</u> appear in the free-body diagram. The orientation of the object is always preserved.

- A coordinate system <u>might</u> appear as well.

Before you can determine which forces belong in a particular free-body diagram, you should familiarize yourself with the contents of the Table of Common Forces in the Appendix. However, there are some simple guidelines to help you draw free-body diagrams, as listed below.

Normal force and friction force: For each surface touching the object there is a normal force and (possibly) a friction force. If the surface is described as being *frictionless*, then the friction force is zero. (**Note:** Sometimes the term *smooth* is used to mean that the surface is frictionless.)

Spring force: For each spring attached to the object, there is (possibly) a spring force. If the spring is neither stretched nor compressed, the spring force is zero.

Gravitational force: Every object in the universe exerts a gravitational force on every other object. However, if the separation of two objects is very large (such as between you and the planet Jupiter), or if both are relatively light (such as you and your neighbor), then we can neglect the effect of gravitation. However large separations can be compensated by large masses, such as the effect that the sun has on the earth. For everyday objects, we usually consider only the nearest celestial object, like the earth, moon, or sun. When objects are called *massless* or *light*, then we ignore the gravitational force on these objects.

Tension force: For each string attached to the object, there is (possibly) a tension force. If the string is described as being *slack*, then the tension force is zero. However, if the string is described as being *taut*, then the tension force is non-zero.

Air resistance force: Whenever an object moves relative to the surrounding air (or other gas), there is an air resistance force. Unless the relative speed between the object and the air is very large, we usually ignore this effect.

Buoyant force: Whenever an object is in a fluid, and both are in a gravitational field, there is a buoyant force. Often, because the density of the fluid (such as air) is much smaller than the density of the object, we can ignore this effect.

The net force. Force is a vector quantity, which means it has both magnitude and direction. The *net force* or *resultant force* is the vector sum of all the forces exerted on a particular object:

$$\mathbf{F}_{net} \equiv \mathbf{F}_1 + \mathbf{F}_2 + \mathbf{F}_3 + \dots \qquad \textbf{definition of net force}$$

where $\mathbf{F}_1$, $\mathbf{F}_2$, ... refer to the individual forces exerted on an object. It is the <u>net</u> force that determines the motion of the object. The net force is not exerted by any one thing and is not a separate force that exists outside of the others. Rather, it is the total effect of all the individual forces. Therefore, a free-body diagram, which shows all the individual forces, should <u>never</u> show the net force as an individual or separate force.

An amusement park ride consists of an airplane on the end of a cable whirled in a horizontal circle, as shown on the left below. We can see that a large cable is used to support the airplane and to keep it moving in a circle. This means there are only two (non-negligible) forces on the airplane: (1) the gravitational force exerted by the earth, and (2) the tension force exerted by the cable. (We have assumed that the air resistance force is small enough to ignore.) The free-body diagram for the airplane is shown below in the middle. The net force is directed toward the center of the horizontal circle, as shown in the *vector-addition diagram*. (You will find out exactly why a little later!) Therefore, the tension force has been drawn just the right size so that when we add these two forces, the resultant is horizontal and toward the center, as shown on the right.

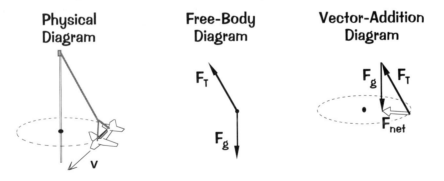

three different diagrams for an amusement-park ride

In the next section, we describe the physical laws governing how the forces exerted on an object affect its motion.

2.2 NEWTON'S LAWS OF MOTION

In 1686, Sir Isaac Newton (1642–1727) published his three laws of motion, which relate the motion of objects (their kinematical behavior or response) to the causes of that motion (the individual forces exerted on the objects). These three laws remain the basis of how scientists view the macroscopic (large-scale) world. We sometimes refer to this view as *Classical Mechanics*.

Mass versus weight. In order to fully understand Newton's laws, we must first make a distinction between the ideas of *mass* and *weight*. Weight is the magnitude of the gravitational force exerted on one object by <u>everything else</u>! Usually this is simply due to the closest celestial object, like the earth or the moon. For most objects a spring scale can be used to measure the object's weight.

Loosely speaking, mass is the "amount of stuff" we have, which does not change when we change locations. It <u>cannot</u> be measured using a spring scale, because then its value would be different at different locations in the universe. Instead, we use an *equal-arm balance* to measure an object's mass.

Consider an object that weighs (about) $5\frac{1}{2}$lb on the earth, or (about) 24N. On a spring scale, let's say the spring stretches by 12cm (that is, it stretches 1cm for every 2N of weight it measures). On an equal-arm balance, it requires $2\frac{1}{2}$ standard "units" of mass to balance our object, so we say that the object has a mass of $2\frac{1}{2}$ kilograms (or kg). (That is, the standard unit of mass is the kilogram.)

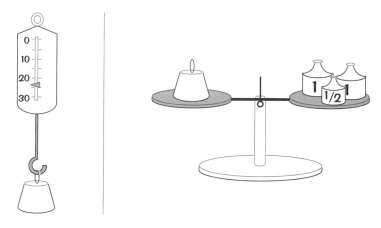

**the weight of an object versus its mass
as measured on the surface of the earth**

On the surface of the moon, we would find some changes. Using the same spring scale we discover that the moon's gravitational pull is weaker, because the spring only stretches by 2cm (instead of 12cm). Therefore, the <u>weight</u> of our object is only 4N on the moon. However, using the same equal-arm balance, we find that the <u>same</u> number of standard units of mass is needed to balance our object. This is because the moon pulls less on our standards by the same proportion that it does on our object. This means our measurement of mass is the same everywhere! (As long as there is a gravitational field!!)

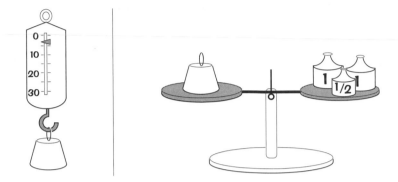

the weight of an object versus its mass
as measured on the surface of the moon

When the mass is measured using an equal-arm balance, it is sometimes referred to as the *gravitational mass*. In the next section, we will use the *inertial mass* to show how forces affect the motion of objects. For now, we will assume that these two are identical, and we will use them interchangeably. We will use the same symbol m to represent each one.

Newton's three laws of motion. We now present Newton's Laws of Motion, restated in modern English. For each law, we provide an explanation and, if possible, a mathematical description.

NEWTON'S FIRST LAW OF MOTION

An object moving at a particular velocity (speed and direction) will remain
at that same velocity until an unbalanced force is exerted on it.

- Remaining at constant velocity means that its motion does not change:

    (1)   An object at rest (stationary) would remain at rest.

    (2)   An object going at a particular speed in a particular direction would simply keep going at that speed in that direction.

- An unbalanced force is needed to change <u>either</u> the speed <u>or</u> the direction of motion.

- When the forces exerted on an object are unbalanced, we say there is a "net force on the object". The net force is the vector sum of all the individual forces exerted on the object.

> *Whenever there is a non-zero net force exerted on an object, the object accelerates in the same direction as the net force. The magnitude of the acceleration is the magnitude of the net force divided by the mass of the object.*

- Mathematically Newton's 2nd law is written:

$$\mathbf{F}_{net} = m\ \mathbf{a}.$$
Newton's 2nd law

  where: $\mathbf{F}_{net}$ = the net force on the object

  = the vector sum of all individual forces

  m = the mass of the object

  $\mathbf{a}$ = the acceleration of the object

  = the vector describing the rate at which the velocity of the object changes

- A net force causes an acceleration, which is recognized by a <u>change</u> in velocity.

- Newton's 2nd law tells us that if the mass of an object is constant, then its acceleration is proportional to the net force exerted on it:

$$\mathbf{a} \propto \mathbf{F}_{net} \quad \text{when } m \text{ is constant.}$$

- The 2nd law also tells us that if the same net force is exerted on different objects, their accelerations are proportional to the inverses of their masses:

$$\mathbf{a} \propto \frac{1}{m} \quad \text{when } \mathbf{F}_{net} \text{ is constant.}$$

  So, the larger an object's mass, the smaller its acceleration.

- Because the tendency <u>not</u> to change is called *inertia*, the mass used in Newton's 2nd law is a measure of an object's inertia, and is sometimes called its *inertial mass*. The inertial mass is assumed to be equal to the *gravitational mass* (the mass used in the empirical law for the gravitational force).

- Whenever the net force on an object is zero, we say that the object is *in equilibrium*, even if it is moving at constant velocity.

NEWTON'S THIRD LAW OF MOTION

> *Whenever one object exerts a force on a second object, the second object always exerts a force on the first. These two forces are equal in magnitude, are opposite in direction, and have the same nature.*

- Mathematically Newton's 3rd law is written:

$$\mathbf{F}_{\text{on 1 by 2}} = -\mathbf{F}_{\text{on 2 by 1}}.$$ **Newton's 3rd law**

   where:

   $$\mathbf{F}_{\text{on 1 by 2}} = \text{the force exerted on object 1 by object 2}$$
   $$\mathbf{F}_{\text{on 2 by 1}} = \text{the force exerted on object 2 by object 1}$$

- These two forces are the two sides of a single interaction, so they are always the same kind of force, such as gravitational, frictional, normal, spring, etc.

- These two forces are sometimes referred to as either *an action/reaction pair* or *an action and its reaction*. Since either one of the forces could be the action and the other the reaction, it is incorrect to think that one of them happens first, followed by the other. <u>Both occur at exactly the same time</u>. If one of them changes, then both of them change, instant by instant.

- Although these two forces add up to zero (mathematically), they do not add up to a net force of zero on any <u>one</u> object. Each is exerted on a <u>different</u> object, so they do not produce equilibrium. That is, these two forces do not balance each other. (In the previous section when we were weighing an object with a spring scale, the spring force *balanced* the gravitational force. Both forces were exerted on the same object, and <u>did</u> produce equilibrium.)

Newton's laws and reference frames. Newton's laws are valid only in <u>some</u> reference frames. For example, imagine a ball hanging from a string inside a railroad car. (See diagram on next page.) When the car is at rest, the ball hangs straight down. The ball is at rest as seen from inside the railroad car, and the net force on it is zero also, thus confirming Newton's 2nd law. When the car is moving with constant velocity, the ball also hangs straight down. As seen from the ground the ball is moving, but as seen from inside the car it is at rest. The net force on the ball is zero, so Newton's 2nd law is again confirmed in both reference frames. However, when the railroad car is accelerating, such as when the wheels are locked in place, the ball hangs at an angle. As seen from the ground, the ball is accelerating, as predicted by Newton's 2nd law. But observations made from inside the railroad car contradict Newton's 2nd law, because now there is clearly a net force on the ball, yet it appears to be at rest inside the car. (Thus, $\mathbf{F}_{\text{net}} \neq m\mathbf{a} = 0$.)

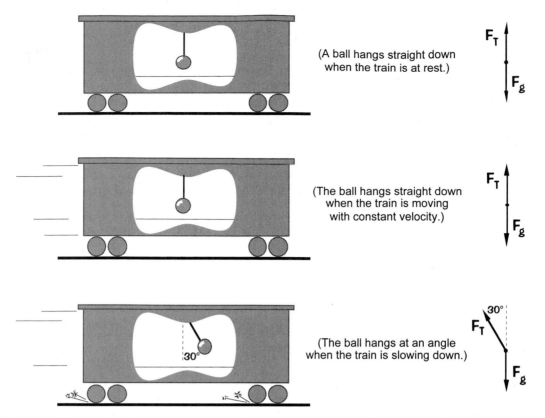

(A ball hangs straight down when the train is at rest.)

(The ball hangs straight down when the train is moving with constant velocity.)

(The ball hangs at an angle when the train is slowing down.)

three different reference frames for observing a ball hanging from a string

A reference frame in which Newton's laws are valid is called an *inertial frame*. The earth is only approximately an inertial frame, because objects that appear to be at rest on the earth are actually accelerating very slightly. The sun is a better inertial frame.

Newton's laws and free-body diagrams. To understand the motion of objects, we usually use Newton's 2nd law written in component form, as shown here:

$$F_{\text{net},x} = ma_x \qquad\qquad F_{\text{net},y} = ma_y$$

where:

$F_{\text{net},x}$ = the component of the net force in the x-direction
= the sum of the x-components of all the individual forces

a_x = the component of the acceleration in the x-direction

$F_{\text{net},y}$ = the component of the net force in the y-direction
= the sum of the y-components of all the individual forces

a_y = the component of the acceleration in the y-direction

If a coordinate system is clearly indicated and oriented on the free-body diagram, it is often straightforward to find the components of each of the forces that make up the net force. Let's go back to our example of the amusement-park ride:

An amusement park ride consists of an airplane on the end of a cable whirled in a horizontal circle. What is the net force on the airplane in the horizontal and vertical directions?

Answer. A free-body diagram is shown to the right. Only the tension force has a component in the horizontal (x) direction. It is ($-F_T \sin30°$). So, the x-component of the net force on the airplane is:

$$F_{\text{net},x} = -F_T \sin30°$$

Both forces have components in the vertical (y) direction, so the y-component of the net force is:

$$F_{\text{net},y} = F_T \cos30° + (-F_g) = F_T \cos30° - F_g$$

In the following pages, we show how dynamics is used either to predict the behavior of objects or to learn about the physical world.

2.3   DYNAMICS

Briefly stated, *dynamics* is the study of the relationship between forces and motion. Using kinematics, we are able to recognize and distinguish situations in which objects are accelerating and those in which they are not. Dynamics enables us to relate the forces exerted on different objects in different situations to the masses of those objects and their motion.

An agenda for dynamics. If we want to be able to say how the motion of an object is affected by the things it interacts with in its surroundings, there are several steps we need to be able to take:

(1)   *Identify forces/interactions.* We must be able to recognize and identify the different kinds of interactions that might occur between objects. In particular, because we express these interactions as forces, we need to know how to determine the direction in which each force is exerted.

(2)   *Measure magnitudes of forces.* We must be able to determine how strongly an interaction affects an object in different situations. In other words, we need to measure forces. (We usually use springs to do this.)

(3)   *Determine / apply / re-evaluate the force laws.* We must find out what each of the force laws depends upon (such as mass, speed, displacement, etc.) so that we can calculate them in different situations. (Of course, we do not make up these rules.

Nature does. Scientists simply try to find out what the rules are and then describe them, usually with equations.) If the observed motion of an object does not correspond to the predicted motion, sometimes we go back and change the details of the force laws to account for the differences.

(4) *Inventory forces.* We need to be able to keep track of all the individual forces exerted on an object. We use a free-body diagram to do this.

(5) *Combine the effects of two or more forces.* We must be able to find the net result when many forces are exerted on a single object. We use vector addition to accomplish this. The result is called the *net force*.

(6) *Relate the behavior of an object to the forces exerted on it.* We must know how the motion of an object is affected by forces. The general rules governing how this happens are called the *laws of motion*. Newton's three laws serve as the general rules in everyday situations. In particular, Newton's 2nd law relates the acceleration of an object to the net force exerted on it.

Kinematics versus dynamics. The study of moving objects requires both kinematics and dynamics. Here we present an overview of both:

Kinematics describes the details of motion—the position, velocity, and acceleration—as well as the relationships between these quantities. For example, knowledge of the initial velocity and the acceleration of something can be used to determine how the velocity and position of the object change over time. Likewise, knowing how the position and velocity change can allow us to determine an object's acceleration.

Dynamics relates changes in motion (accelerations) to the combinations of forces or interactions that cause those changes. Thus, knowledge of acceleration can be used to determine the net force exerted on an object, and knowledge of forces can be used to determine force laws. Likewise, knowledge of force laws allows us to predict the net force exerted on an object, and knowledge of the net force allows us to predict the acceleration of the object.

Reasoning with Newton's laws. Clearly all of these quantities (position, velocity, displacement, acceleration, force, net force, mass, etc.) are related to each other. Therefore, you must be very flexible in how you reason about them and with them. Sometimes you will use knowledge of an object's motion to learn something about the forces exerted on it. At other times, you will use knowledge of the forces exerted on an object to learn something about its behavior. In the following, we present some examples of how we use Newton's laws to learn about different situations.

EQUILIBRIUM SITUATIONS

Whenever the acceleration of an object is zero—that is, when the object is at rest or moving with constant velocity—we say that the object is in *equilibrium*. By Newton's 2nd law, we know that the net force on any object in equilibrium is zero, which means that all the forces exerted on the object are balanced. If we know some of the forces exerted in a situation, we can often deduce values or relative sizes for the other forces. For instance, consider an object that hangs at rest from a spring scale. A spring scale reads the value of the upward force exerted on an object by the spring, in this case, 24N. Because the net force on the object is zero, we deduce that the gravitational force on the object is 24N downward. We say that the weight of the object is 24N. (We have ignored the buoyant force in this situation, because the density of our object is assumed to be much larger than the density of air.)

A book weighing 5N is placed on an adjustable incline as shown. What can we say about the forces exerted on the book? In particular, what are they, and how do they compare to each other?

Answer. We are told that the book weighs 5N, so we know that the earth exerts a gravitational force on it. Also, the book is touching a surface, so there must be a normal force and a friction force exerted by each surface. The book is not moving relative to the surface, so the friction force is static friction.

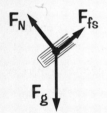

The normal force points directly away from the surface, and the static friction force points parallel to the surface. Therefore, there are three forces exerted on the book — denoted F_g, F_N, and F_{fs} — as shown in the free-body diagram at left.

The book is at rest, so the velocity is constant, and the acceleration of the book is zero. Therefore, by Newton's 2nd law, the net force on the book is zero also, and the three forces must add up to zero. This is shown pictorially on the right.

These three forces form a right triangle, with the gravitational force as the hypotenuse, and the normal and static friction forces as the legs. We know that the legs of a right triangle are always smaller than the hypotenuse, and we know that the lengths of the directed line segments are proportional to the magnitudes of the forces. Therefore, of the three forces, the gravitational force must be the largest. Because of the particular angle (38°), we know also that the normal force is larger than the static friction force. (Mathematically, we get $F_g > F_N > F_{fs}$.)

A block of wood is pulled at constant speed by a light rope as shown. What can we say about the forces exerted in this situation?

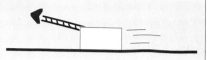

Answer. A string is attached to the block, so there is a tension force exerted on it. The direction of the tension force is the same as the angle of the rope. We assume the block has mass, so there is a gravitational force exerted by the earth. Its direction is straight down. The block is touching a surface, so there is a normal force (pointing straight upward) and a friction force. The block is sliding on the surface, so it is a kinetic friction force. Its direction is opposite the velocity of the block relative to the surface, so it points to the right. Thus, there are 4 individual forces exerted on the block, with directions as shown in the diagram below.

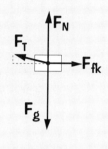

Let's look first at the forces having vertical components. There are three: (1) the normal force exerted by the horizontal surface, (2) the gravitational force exerted by the earth, and (3) the tension force exerted by the rope. The block is traveling at constant velocity, so its acceleration is zero ($a_x = a_y = 0$). Then, by Newton's 2nd law (in the vertical direction) the sum of the vertical components of all the forces exerted on the block must be zero. Therefore, the gravitational force must be slightly larger than the normal force (by an amount equal to the vertical component of the tension force). (Mathematically, $F_g > F_N$.)

Now let's look in the horizontal direction. There are only two forces that have components in the horizontal direction, the tension force and the kinetic friction force exerted by the surface. The acceleration of the block is zero. Therefore, by Newton's 2nd law, the horizontal component of the net force is zero also. So, the component of the tension force in the horizontal direction must be equal (in magnitude) to the kinetic friction force. As long as the rope is not horizontal, we know that each of the components of the tension force is smaller than the tension force itself. (We know that the legs of a right triangle are smaller than the hypotenuse.) Therefore, we can say also that the kinetic friction force is smaller than the tension force. ($F_{fk} < F_T$.)

Keep in mind that although the block in this example is moving, its acceleration is zero, so this is an equilibrium situation.

NON-EQUILIBRIUM SITUATIONS

Whenever the acceleration of an object is <u>not</u> zero, we have a non-equilibrium situation. The reasoning we use to analyze these situations is similar to the reasoning we used for equilibrium situations, except that now we must take into account the object's non-zero acceleration. Consider the following example. (Note: Because the situation is so similar to the previous situation, you should keep in mind what happened previously, and compare those results to the ones coming up. You should ask yourself, "What changes? Why does it change? What stays the same? Why?")

A block of wood is pulled by a light rope as shown, speeding up as it moves to the left. What can we say about the forces exerted in this situation? (What are they, and how do they compare?)

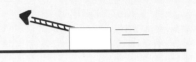

Answer. There are 4 forces exerted on the wooden block, as shown in the free-body diagram below. Even though the wooden block is accelerating, there is no component of the acceleration vector in the vertical direction $(a_x \neq 0; a_y = 0)$. Therefore, the analysis for the vertical direction is the same as it was when the block was in equilibrium. The gravitational force must be slightly larger than the normal force by an amount equal to the vertical component of the tension force. $(F_g > F_N.)$

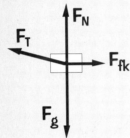

Now let's look in the horizontal direction. There are only two forces that have components in the horizontal direction, and the acceleration of the block is non-zero. It is to the left. Therefore, by Newton's 2nd law, the horizontal component of the net force is non-zero also. So, the horizontal component of the tension force must be larger (in magnitude) than the kinetic friction force. Because the component of F_T must be smaller than F_T itself, we know also that the tension force is larger than the friction force. $(F_T > F_{fk}.)$

Solving problems with Newton's laws. The goal of this approach to learning physics is two-fold: (1) to help you to understand the individual concepts (such as position, velocity, mass, force, and acceleration) and the principles (the relationships between concepts, such as Newton's 2nd and 3rd laws) needed to analyze and to reason about different physical situations; and (2) to help you use your analysis and reasoning skills to solve problems. In our view, analysis and reasoning about a problem situation are an important first step to solving problems. Once the situation is analyzed, equations may be applied properly to finish the problem. Consider the following two examples.

A 2.3kg dictionary slides along a floor having a coefficient of kinetic friction of 0.2. If the initial speed of the dictionary is 4.2m/s, how far will it slide before coming to rest?

Answer. First we must identify which forces are exerted on the dictionary. The earth exerts a gravitational force pointing straight down. The floor exerts a normal force pointing straight up and a kinetic friction force pointing to the left. The free-body diagram for the dictionary is shown below.

Now let's analyze the situation. Using Newton's 2nd law (in the vertical direction) tells us that the normal force is equal to the gravitational force. ($F_N = F_g$) Applying our knowledge of the empirical law for the gravitational force tells us that $F_g = mg = 23$N. Therefore, $F_N = 23$N.

The only force with a horizontal component is the kinetic friction force. To find the magnitude of this force, we use another empirical law, $F_{fk} = \mu_k F_N = (0.2)(23\text{N}) = 4.6$N. Because $F_{net,x} = -F_{fk} = -4.6$N, we get $a_x = -2$m/s^2. We now use kinematics to find the total distance traveled by the dictionary.

The time needed to slow down to zero is found using the definition of acceleration:

$$a_x = \frac{\Delta v_x}{\Delta t} = \text{slope of } v_x \text{ vs. } t$$

so:

$$\Delta t = \frac{\Delta v_x}{a_x} = \frac{0\text{m/s} - 4.2\text{m/s}}{-2\text{m/s}^2} = 2.1\text{s},$$

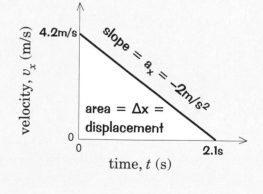

as shown in the graph to the right.

The displacement is the area below v_x vs. t:

$$\Delta x = \tfrac{1}{2}(4.2\text{m/s})(2.1\text{s}) = \textbf{4.4m}.$$

This can be verified using the equation $\Delta x = v_{0x}\Delta t + \frac{1}{2}a_x(\Delta t)^2$.

For this example, we used empirical laws and given information to calculate a value for the net force exerted on the dictionary. Then we used $\mathbf{F}_{net} = m\mathbf{a}$ to find its acceleration, and kinematics to predict changes in its position and velocity. In the next example, we do just the opposite!

A dictionary (mass unknown) slides 2.5m along a floor before coming to rest. If the initial speed of the dictionary is 4.4m/s, what is the coefficient of kinetic friction between the dictionary and the floor?

Answer. As in the previous example, there are 3 forces exerted on the dictionary, as shown in the free-body diagram. To find the coefficient of kinetic friction, we need to determine the kinetic friction force and the normal force. Analysis of the vertical direction tells us that the normal force is equal to the gravitational force ($F_N = F_g$). Knowledge of the empirical law for the gravitational force tells us that $F_g = mg$. Therefore, $F_N = mg$.

The only force with a horizontal component is the kinetic friction force. To find its magnitude, we must use Newton's 2nd law:

$$F_{net,x} = -F_{fk} = ma_x,$$

which means: $\qquad F_{fk} = -ma_x.$

The ratio of these two forces (F_{fk} and F_N) is the coefficient of kinetic friction:

$$\mu_k = \frac{F_{fk}}{F_N} = \frac{-ma_x}{mg} = -\frac{a_x}{g}.$$

Unfortunately, we do not yet know the acceleration of the dictionary. To find it we must use kinematics. A sketch of v_x vs. t will help us determine the acceleration from the given information.

The area below v_x vs. t is the displacement, given as 2.5m, and the slope of v_x vs. t is the acceleration, which is our desired unknown. In terms of Δt, the time interval during which the dictionary stops, we get:

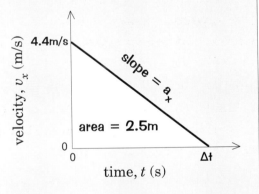

$$\text{area} = \frac{1}{2}(4.4\text{m/s})\,\Delta t = 2.5\text{m}$$

$$\text{slope} = \frac{0\text{m/s} - 4.4\text{m/s}}{\Delta t} = a_x$$

Solving for the acceleration of the dictionary, we get $a_x = -3.87\text{m/s}^2$. Using a value of $g = 10\text{N/kg} = 10\text{m/s}^2$, we get $\mu_k = \mathbf{0.39}$.

(Did you notice that we did not need to know the mass of the dictionary in order to find the coefficient of friction?)

In this example, we used given information about the displacement and velocity of the dictionary to calculate the dictionary's acceleration. Then we used $\mathbf{F}_{net} = m\mathbf{a}$ (this time) to learn something about the forces and physical characteristics of the situation.

As you can see, there are many different types of problem-solving steps needed to solve these problems. In the figure to the right, we represent different aspects of problem solving. For example, starting at the top and using the arrow on the left-hand side, we show that you can find the acceleration of an object using kinematics if you know some details of the object's motion, such as its position as a function of time. Notice how each step or process can go in either direction, up or down. The actual direction used in any particular problem depends on the problem. Efficient and effective problem solving involves being able to use any process in whatever direction is needed to find the desired unknown.

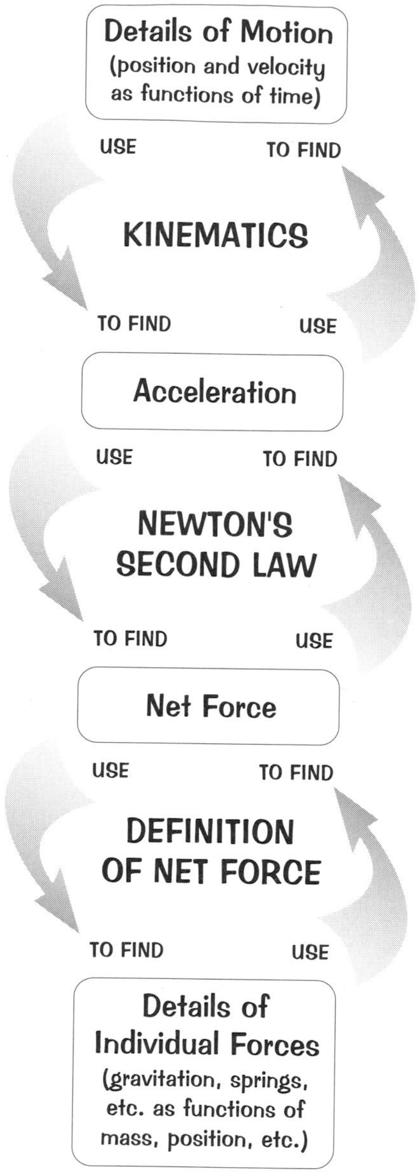

Summary. *Dynamics* is the method physicists use to relate knowledge of the forces exerted on an object to knowledge of its motion. Analysis and reasoning about physical systems allows scientists and engineers to understand and make predictions about the systems they are studying. There are many individual skills needed to understand dynamics, such as how to draw and use a free-body diagram and how to reason using Newton's laws. You will need to work hard to develop these skills. However, the ability to perform these tasks helps anyone to break down and analyze any system in terms of the objects contained in that system and the interactions between them.

Details of Motion
(position and velocity as functions of time)

USE   TO FIND

KINEMATICS

TO FIND   USE

Acceleration

USE   TO FIND

NEWTON'S SECOND LAW

TO FIND   USE

Net Force

USE   TO FIND

DEFINITION OF NET FORCE

TO FIND   USE

Details of Individual Forces
(gravitation, springs, etc. as functions of mass, position, etc.)

relationship between details of an object's motion and details of individual forces

Limitations of dynamics. In everyday situations involving large-scale objects, Newton's laws are always and completely valid. If you know the force laws, then you can find the net force. If you know the net force you can find the acceleration. Unfortunately, knowing the acceleration is not always enough to predict the position and velocity of an object at a later time. The reason is that you must know the acceleration as a function of time. Therefore, either the net force must be constant, or you must know the net force at all times. These are the only conditions under which you have sufficient mathematics to predict the motion of an object.

What if you do not know the net force as a function of time? For example, when a bomb explodes, what forces are exerted on the fragments? Can we predict the motion of the individual fragments? It turns out that the motion of the fragments depends on their masses, and we can predict certain features of their motion without knowing the exact force law governing their interactions. Here are some situations in which <u>you cannot</u> use dynamics to predict the exact motion of the objects interacting.

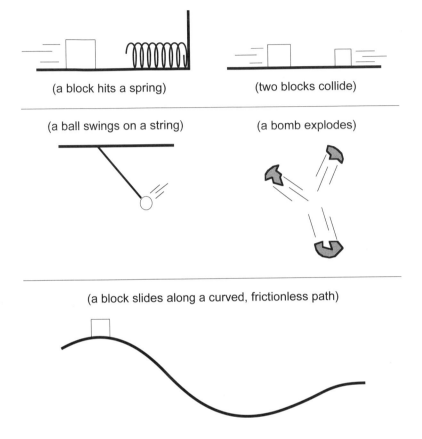

(a block hits a spring)   (two blocks collide)

(a ball swings on a string)   (a bomb explodes)

(a block slides along a curved, frictionless path)

situations in which the motion cannot be determined using dynamics alone

For some situations, such as objects hitting springs and objects moving along curved paths, we will use *energy* ideas to understand them better. For situations involving collisions and explosions, we will find that *momentum* is an important idea. Most importantly, we will show that these quantities are *conserved*, which means that momentum and energy may have different distributions among the objects in the universe, but the amount of each must remain constant <u>at all times</u>.

Conclusion. Dynamics and kinematics are extremely useful for analyzing physical situations and solving problems. Even though you will soon be using new ideas and concepts to learn about physical situations, what you have learned so far will continue to be important for understanding these situations and for applying new concepts properly.

Appendix: Table of Common Forces

In this appendix, we provide descriptions of the following forces:

Contact Forces: normal, tension, spring (or elastic), buoyant, friction (kinetic and static), and air resistance (or drag).

Action-at-a-Distance Forces: gravitational (local and universal), electrostatic (or electrical), and magnetic.

Contact Forces

Force Symbol Force Law or Relationship	Description	When is the force present?
Normal Force F_N (There is <u>no</u> general formula for determining F_N; you must use dynamics to determine its value.)	Whenever two objects press against each other, the constraint force that the surface of each exerts against the surface of the other is called a *normal* force. A normal force always points at right angles to and away from the surface that exerts the force. (In mathematics, the word *normal* means *perpendicular*.) The normal force has no specific force law (a formula that tells you what the force depends on); you must calculate the magnitude of a normal force from other information provided in the problem, such as the motion of the object and the other forces exerted on it. We usually assume that objects exerting a normal force do not deform as a result.	Whenever two objects are touching, each will exert a normal force on the other, no matter whether one of the objects is actively pushing (such as when a person presses down on a table) or just blocking the motion of the other object (such as when a table is holding up a book). The normal force always pushes; it never pulls. We can consider it zero when the two objects are still touching, but are just on the verge of separating.
Tension Force F_T (There is <u>no</u> general formula for determining F_T; you must use dynamics to determine its value.)	The *tension* force is the constraint force that a flexible cord, rope, wire or string exerts on an object by pulling on it. Because they are flexible, strings cannot push. Tension forces, like normal forces, have no specific force law; you must calculate them from other information provided in the problem. A cord always lines up in the direction it is pulling, so the direction of the tension force is always along the cord exerting it. For most problems, you can assume that the mass of a cord can be ignored and that the cord does not stretch, deform or break.	Whenever a cord is attached to an object, the cord will exert a tension force (unless the cord is *slack*). The tension force is non-zero whenever the cord is *taut* (or *in tension* or *under tension*). In many situations, the tension force is measured using a spring scale.

(continued on the next page)

Contact Forces (continued)

Force
Symbol
Force Law or
Relationship	Description	When is the force present?

Spring Force
(also called **Elastic Force**)

$F_s = k\left| l - l_0 \right|$
(Hooke's Law)

(*l* is the length of the spring, and l_0 is the relaxed length of the spring.) | The *spring* force is the force exerted by a spring that is stretched or compressed. The force law for springs is called *Hooke's Law* and states that the spring force is proportional to the change in length of the spring from its *relaxed* or unstretched state. The proportionality constant *k*, called the *spring constant*, tells how much force must be exerted to produce each unit of change in $\left| l - l_0 \right|$. It is a measure of the "stiffness" of the spring being used. The direction of the force is always toward the relaxed position of the end of the spring. That is, a stretched spring pulls on objects attached to its end, and a compressed spring pushes. Hooke's law is only accurate when the spring is neither stretched nor compressed too far from its relaxed length. | A spring force will be present any time a spring is stretched or compressed. Some other elastic objects (like rubber bands) may obey Hooke's law for a limited range of stretching, but cannot be compressed.

General Comments:
• When $l < l_0$, the spring pushes.
• When $l > l_0$, the spring pulls.
• The spring constant is usually the same for both compression and stretching.
• Most ropes, strings, etc. behave like springs with very large spring constants.

Buoyant Force

$F_B =$ (total weight of the fluid displaced by the object) | The *buoyant* force is the force exerted by fluid (liquid or gas) in contact with the object. There must be a gravitational field to have buoyancy. For liquids, the buoyant force is caused by the dependence of the pressure on depth (such as the pressure in the oceans increasing with increasing depth). For gases, the force is caused by the dependence of the pressure on altitude (such as air pressure <u>decreasing</u> at increasing heights above the earth's surface). The direction of the buoyant force is always opposite the direction of the local gravitational force. | The buoyant force is present whenever the object is fully or partially immersed in a fluid, <u>and</u> both are in a gravitational field. If the object is much denser than the fluid(s) surrounding it, we usually ignore the buoyant force.

A buoyant force is also present when the fluid is accelerating.

Force Symbol Force Law or Relationship	Description	When is the force present?

Friction Forces

Kinetic:
$F_{fk} = \mu_k F_N$

Static:
$F_{fs,max} = \mu_s F_N$

— or —

$F_{fs} \leq \mu_s F_N$

(In general, you must use dynamics to determine the value of F_{fs}. Only when you are sure that the force of static friction is at its maximum value can you use the empirical law.)

Description

Sliding or Kinetic: Whenever two objects slide over each other (with one or both in motion — such as a block sliding down an incline), each exerts a force on the other called the *sliding friction* or *kinetic friction* force (*kinetic* means *in motion*). The direction of the force on each object is always along (parallel to) the surface and opposes that object's sliding. Its magnitude depends on how hard the surfaces press together (the normal force) and on the roughness or other resistive properties of the two surfaces touching. (These properties determine the value of the coefficient of sliding friction μ_k.) F_{fk} usually does not depend on the surface area in contact or the velocities of the objects in contact.

Static: If two objects are not sliding, each may exert a *static friction* force on the other — a constraint force that prevents sliding. The objects act as though they are "stuck" together. For example, a car parked on a hillside remains stationary because the road exerts a static friction force on its tires; if the hill were icy, the static friction force might not be strong enough to keep the car from sliding. Like the normal force, the magnitude of the static friction force can have any value up to some maximum. Just as too great a force on a wooden board will break the board, too great a downhill force on the car will unstick it from its stationary position. Like the sliding friction force, the *maximum value* of the static friction force depends on both the normal force and the resistive properties (roughness, etc.) of the two surfaces in contact. The direction of the force is opposite to the direction the object "wants" to slide (i.e., opposite the direction the object would slide if there were no friction).

When is the force present?

Kinetic friction will be present whenever two surfaces slide across each other (such as an object on a large surface or two objects in contact with each other).

Objects with surfaces in contact exert static friction forces on each other only when these forces are needed to keep them moving (or not moving) as though they were a single object (as though they are "stuck" together). They become "unstuck" when the net force due to all the other forces exceeds $\mu_s F_N$. Then the friction force becomes kinetic.

General Comments:
• Two surfaces only exert one kind of friction force on each other at a time: it must be either kinetic or static friction.
• Slippery surfaces sometimes exert friction forces so small that they make no difference to a problem, so you can ignore them (i.e., you can let them equal zero). We refer to these surfaces as *frictionless* or *ideal*.
• In everyday usage, *smooth* means *not rough* or *even*, and some smooth materials (such as rubber) exert friction forces. In physics, we often use *smooth* to mean *frictionless*.
• For any pair of surfaces in contact, the value of μ_s is always larger than the value of μ_k.
• Friction is a *resistive* force because it always works against the relative motion of the objects in contact.

(continued on the next page)

Force Symbol Force Law or Relationship	Description	When is the force present?
Air Resistance Force (also called **Drag Force**) $F_{air} = Av^2$ (at speeds we normally encounter)	The *air resistance* or *drag force* is the force that the air (or another gas) exerts to oppose the motion of an object moving through it. It depends on the object's shape (a sheet of paper falls differently when it is flat than when it is crumpled into a ball), and it increases as the object speeds up. It depends on the object's velocity <u>relative to the surrounding air</u>, so if wind is present, an object may experience air resistance without moving! The direction of the force opposes the object's motion relative to the air. The shape parameter (or shape factor) A depends on the shape and cross-sectional area of the object, as well as the density of the surrounding air (or other gas).	An object experiences air resistance whenever it moves through the air (or any other gas) or there is wind blowing on the object. In many problems, the object is small enough (so that the shape factor A is very small) or moving slowly enough relative to the air that air resistance is much smaller than the other forces in the problem, and you can ignore it. Even in cases where air resistance is non-negligible, such as firing cannonballs large distances, air resistance is often ignored for simplicity.

Force
Symbol
Force Law or
Relationship   Description   When is the force present?

Gravitational Force

Gravitational forces are the attractive forces that any two objects having mass exert on each other. Unless both objects are very massive (such as the earth and the sun) or one is very massive and they are very close to each other (such as when an object is near the surface of the earth), gravitational forces are too weak for us to detect without the use of extremely sensitive instruments. For now, we will deal only with the gravitational force that the earth exerts on objects near its surface; this force approximately equals the object's mass times the gravitational constant g. The "average" value of g on the earth is about 9.8N/kg.

(near the surface of the earth)

$F_g = mg$

Objects with mass always exert a gravitational force on each other. There is no exception. The gravitational force is called an "action-at-a-distance" force because one object (such as the earth) can exert a gravitational force on another object without actually touching it. The gravitational force is always *attractive* (the force on one object is always directly toward the other object); it is <u>never</u> *repulsive*.

(for two point objects)

$F_g = G \dfrac{m_1 m_2}{r^2}$

(Universal Law of Gravitation)

(m_1 and m_2 are the masses of the two objects interacting; r is their separation.)

For other situations—such as rockets leaving the earth, objects deep inside the earth, and planets orbiting the sun—a more complicated (but more general) force law applies. It is the *Universal Law of Gravitation*. G has a value of 6.67×10^{-11}N-m^2/kg^2. For non-point objects, such as the earth and objects on the earth, we can usually use the centers of the objects to measure the separation r. Using the radius of the earth ($R_E = 6.37 \times 10^6$m) and the mass of the earth ($M_E = 5.98 \times 10^{24}$kg), we can show that on the surface of the earth, the gravitational force on an object is:

$$F_g = m \left(\dfrac{GM_E}{R_E{}^2} \right),$$

where m is the mass of the object near the earth. Note that the expression in parentheses multiplying m has a value of 9.8N/kg, as expected! Therefore, close to the surface of the earth, at <u>any</u> position on the earth, we can use $F_g = mg$.

<u>Comments</u>:

Local gravitation. Near the surface of a planet, we can usually determine an approximate law to find the gravitational forces on different objects. The force will always depend upon the mass of the object, but the value of g will depend on the radius and the total mass of the planet.

Universal gravitation. To find the total gravitational force on an object, you must add (vectorially) the individual gravitational forces that each part of one object exerts on each part of the other object.

(continued on the next page)

Force Symbol Force Law or Relationship	Description	When is the force present?
Electrostatic Force (for two point objects) $F_c = k \dfrac{q_1 q_2}{r^2}$ (Coulomb's Law) (q_1 and q_2 are the charges of the two objects interacting; r is their separation.)	*Electrostatic* or *electrical forces* are exerted by one electrically charged object on another. Objects with excess electrons are negatively charged; those with too few are positively charged. Oppositely charged objects attract each other; those with like charges repel each other. One way objects can become electrically charged is by rubbing against each other, so that electrons are transferred from one object to the other. This happens to synthetic fabrics in your clothes dryer, so that garments stick to each other ("static cling"). The electric force is different from the magnetic force. To find the net electrical force between two objects, you must add the individual electrical forces due to each pair of charged particles, one from each object. If the objects are spherical and the charge is distributed evenly, then the net electrical force is given by: $$F_c = k \frac{Q_1 Q_2}{r^2}$$ where Q_1 and Q_2 are the total charges on each of the objects, and r is the separation of their centers.	Bodies that are electrically charged, or that are neutral but have uneven distributions of charge, exert electrostatic forces on each other. All large-scale objects, such as the earth or people or pieces of wood, contain vast numbers of negative and positive charges. However, because these charges are usually found in equal amounts evenly distributed throughout the object, there is no net electrical force. In these usual situations we ignore the electrical force.
Magnetic Force (The relationship is beyond the scope of this course.)	*Magnetic forces* are exerted by one magnetic pole on another. Opposite poles (north and south) attract. Like poles repel. The force depends on the strength of the poles, and is stronger when the poles are closer together.	Magnets exert magnetic forces on one another and on certain materials (especially iron) that act like magnets in their presence. (Although we will not worry about them in this course, wires carrying electric currents also exert magnetic forces.)